Berlitz

English

Science
& Technology

Berlitz Languages, Inc.
Princeton, NJ
USA

For use exclusively in connection with Berlitz classroom instruction

Berlitz Languages, Inc.
293 Wall Street
Princeton, NJ
USA

Contents

Contents

Introduction

Science & Technology is designed for students at an upper intermediate to advanced level, who wish to improve their English proficiency in the fields of science and technology.

The programme consists of twelve chapters, which cover subjects such as the impact of technology on everyday life, climate and natural resources, and contemporary health issues.

An audio cassette containing dialogues, interviews, and discussions accompanies the programme.

Role plays, transcriptions of the recordings, and a key containing the answers to the written exercises are found at the back of the book.

We hope this programme will help to make the use of English in science and technology a productive and enjoyable experience.

1

Technology and development

When you have finished this chapter you should be able to

■ understand and take part in discussions about how technology is used, particularly by developing economies

■ express your own views on the applications of science and technology, especially in regard to environmental and social problems

■ understand and use a range of terms employed in specialist discussions of these matters

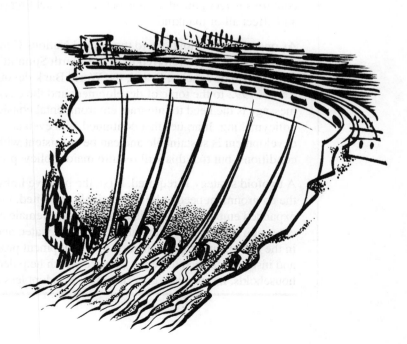

1.1

Warm-up

How has the West been overexploiting the resources of poorer countries?

In what ways are the richer countries imposing inappropriate technologies on developing societies?

Can economic development be achieved without harming the environment?

**1.2
TEXT**

How can industrial and developing societies work together to solve economic and environmental problems?

Environment and development

Traditionally, environmental concerns were limited to the effects of urban and industrial waste disposal on local populations. Now, however, the range of critical issues is far wider. Global warming (also known as the greenhouse effect) and damage to the ozone layer threaten unknown climatic changes, while tropical deforestation contributes to climatic change and also removes permanently from the globe an unknown number of potentially useful species. Transboundary movement of hazardous wastes, acid rain, soil erosion, desertification, threats to indigenous people and overuse of pesticides are further environmental threats.

This changing agenda of environmental issues has led to a rapid evolution in the way these problems are addressed. Partnership between industrial and developing countries is recognized as indispensable to tackling problems that know no borders and affect all of mankind.

As one of its contributions to the United Nations Conference on Environment and Development, often referred to as the 'Earth Summit', which was held in June 1992 in Rio de Janeiro, Brazil, the World Bank devoted its World Development Report 1992 to the topic of development and the environment. The report's main message is the need to integrate environmental considerations into development policymaking. It argues that continued, and even accelerated, economic and human development is sustainable and can be consistent with improving environmental conditions, but that this will require major policy, program and institutional shifts.

A twofold strategy is required. First, the positive links between income growth and the environment need to be aggressively exploited. For example, this calls for expanded emphasis on population programs, female education, agricultural extension and research, sanitation and clean water, and for more local participation in the design and implementation of development programs. Second, strong policies and institutions need to be put in place which help decision makers – corporations, households, farmers and governments – to adopt less damaging forms of behavior.

World Bank Information Brief

2

**1.3
TASK**

Fill each space in this paragraph with the correct form of a noun or verb derived from the words in the box:

The _____ of natural resources and the environmental changes that the earth seems to be _____ present serious dangers to mankind. Although many feel that the threat of global warming has been _____ , there is no doubt that the _____ processes cause widespread concern. These issues are particularly significant for the world's _____ regions. For example, the _____ of land for farming and the destruction of tropical forests may set off climatic changes which could ultimately _____ the environment. Fortunately, the publicity given to these matters has increased our _____ of the threat and our awareness of the human _____ involved. Our responsibility for natural resources cannot be _____ .

overexploit	overuse	understand
overlook	overwhelm	undertake
undergo	overstate	underdevelop
underlie		

**1.4
TASK**

Match the environmental problems listed on the right with their probable causes:

- deforestation
- intensive farming
- energy production

ozone depletion
the greenhouse effect
acid rain
soil erosion
overuse of pesticides
desertification
hazardous waste

**1.5
ANALYSIS**

Over-population and poverty are both cited as root causes of environmental problems. How do they affect the three sources of environmental problems mentioned above?

1.6

What kinds of development policies would be most likely to help governments, communities and companies to adopt less damaging forms of behaviour?

1.7 The **Human Development Index (HDI)** is a statistic originated by *The Economist*, combining each country's GDP per head with its adult literacy rate and life expectancy. The scale runs from 1 – 100: 0 – 49 indicates low development, 50 – 79 medium development, 80 and over high development.

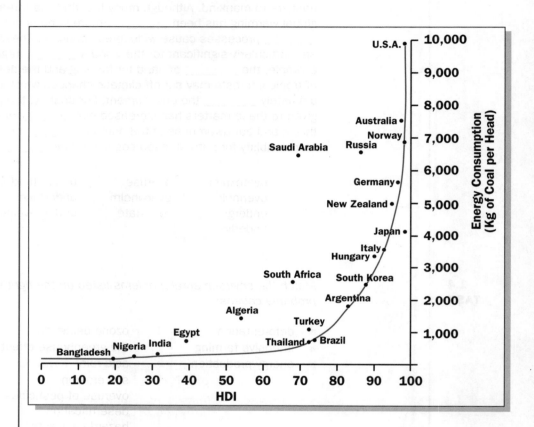

Study the graph then use it to prepare a presentation in which you address the following three points:

1   To what extent is energy consumption a good measure of environmental damage?
2   Why do some countries deviate radically from the curve?
3   Why do you think Japan's energy consumption figure is low compared to that of other highly developed countries?

1.8 The author of 'Environment and development' believes in "the positive links between income growth and the environment". Does the graph on the page opposite support or challenge this belief?

1.9

Industry creates jobs and can bring a country wealth, but it is the chief cause of pollution. How can we balance these needs? In the recording, specialists discuss the concept of 'tradeable permits' in pollution and consider the possibility of moving pollution from developed to less developed countries.

Note these key words and phrases:

trad(e)able	to press ahead
permit	issue
pollution	(gross) national product
CO_2 (carbon dioxide)	to trade on
incentive	access to...
realistic	developed/developing/
	less developed countries

1.10 TASK

Complete the following sentences:

1 Tradeable permits in pollution would allow companies in developing countries...
2 Developing countries should be able to trade... without...
3 The costs and difficulties of getting rid of pollution will be lower...
4 Because the developed countries now have very high levels of pollution,...

1.11 If a system of tradeable permits worked as suggested in the recording, what effect would it have on the shape of the graph on the opposite page?

Should local communities in the developing world be given the opportunity to choose their essential technologies?

Users must be choosers

Ever since the discovery of fire, technologies have been constantly evolving. Technology is determined primarily by need – for greater convenience, higher productivity, improved quality of life or higher income – and each society has developed its own technologies accordingly.

The level of technological development of a society is generally taken to reflect its level of economic and industrial development. The more sophisticated and specialized the technologies, the more advanced that society is considered to be. The 'modernization' theory of development, which still dominates much of the formal development debate, argues that Northern technology is needed for economic development in the South. However, the introduction of advanced technologies is no guarantee of their success, nor of their suitability. Technologies that are appropriate evolve in response to social, cultural and economic circumstances. What is appropriate in one set of circumstances, or from one point of view, may not be so from another.

This raises the question of who chooses. Any technological development makes demands on its users, and so it is the users – the intended beneficiaries – who should decide whether or not it is appropriate to their circumstances and needs. Users must be choosers, and users' participation in the decision-making process is vital if choice is to be appropriate.

Technology choice begins with information. An informed decision demands an understanding of the needs a technology is intended to serve, knowledge of available options and awareness of the techniques, skills and resources necessary for its adoption. Choice of technology also implies access to the tools, techniques, resources, knowledge and the organizational capacity required.

Given the opportunity, anyone can make rational choices. However, people do not always have that opportunity. In many ways, choice is denied: sometimes unwittingly, at other times intentionally. Users are not given the opportunity of becoming choosers because their opinions are not sought, because they do not have access to information, or because it is in the interests of those in power to maintain the lower status of sections of society. The ultimate effect is to hinder rather than stimulate development.

Small World

**1.13
TASK**

Rewrite the following sentences using the words given in capitals:

Example: Choice of technology implies that people can make use of required tools and techniques. ACCESS
*Choice of technology implies **access** to required tools and techniques.*

1   The introduction of advanced technologies is no guarantee of their success, nor of their stability. EITHER/OR
2   However, people do not always have that opportunity. FREQUENTLY
3   Users are not given the opportunity of becoming choosers, because their opinions are not sought. DENIED/BECOME/NOBODY

**1.14
TASK**

Make adjectives from the nouns in capitals and choose an appropriate noun to complete the sentences:

Example: Severe CLIMATE _____ may result from global warming.
*Severe **climatic change** may result from global warming.*

1   The company was fined heavily for dumping HAZARD _____ .
2   ENVIRONMENT _____ have become a major concern among the developed countries.
3   The World Bank's report called for increased AGRICULTURE _____ .
4   Most TECHNOLOGY _____ makes some kind of demand on its users.
5   One of the World Bank's objectives is to promote ECONOMY _____ .

1.15

The text on page 6 gives three reasons for users being denied choice. Which of these reasons do you consider most significant, judging from your own reading or experience?

**1.16
ROLE PLAY**

The sales director of a large Western civil engineering company (Role **A** – page 122) tries to convince a committed environmentalist aid worker (Role **B** – page 124) that developing nations need Western technologies if they are to become economically competitive.

1.17
TEXT

Is the World Bank's technocratic approach to the developing world fundamentally wrong?

The World Bank — a world threat?

The World Bank – the world's best-known and most important agency for economic growth and recovery, lending $24 billion a year to less developed economies – was created in 1944, in the midst of war, by delegates of 43 nations meeting at the New England resort of Bretton Woods. In the decades since then it has helped to generate much economic development. But how relevant are its attitudes and policies to the present-day needs of the world's economies?

In a book published in 1994, *Mortgaging the Earth*, Bruce Rich, an international development policy expert, argues that the World Bank has been 'a prime accomplice in a quiet war against the diversity of humankind's cultures and our planet's biological inheritance.'

Where did the bank go wrong? In Rich's view, it set a technocratic agenda, pushing large, capital-intensive technologies – dams, highways, bridges and the like – and using top-down planning processes to decide lending priorities. Many millions of acres of tropical forests were devastated by projects that exploited the land for cash crops, commercial forestry and cattle raising, while other projects promoted technologies that were unsuitable for local social and economic conditions. (Of 82 agricultural projects listed in a 1989 bank review, 45% had not met their objectives.) Local populations also suffered: implementation of the bank's policies displaced millions in less developed societies, trapping them in poverty and polluting their environment – over 20 million, according to Rich, in India alone since 1947.

Rich sees the fundamental defect in the bank's planning as Western-style centralization, which cannot effectively relieve poverty or create forms of sustainable development that will accord with the environment. A more productive policy would offer smaller-scale aid programs, emphasizing low-impact technologies more suited to local socioeconomic needs. Lending, Rich argues, should be slowed down and the bank made more accessible and responsive: an alternative network of agencies should be set up to make small loans to communities and businesses. Even more radically, he urges that Western nations should stop using the bank to manage Third World debt; they should simply forgive that debt.

**1.18
TASK**

Fill in each space with the correct form of a phrasal verb from the box below:

The arguments _____ by Bruce Rich start from his view that the World Bank's policies have _____ economic progress in developing societies and may even have _____ their cultural decline. Western-style planning has _____ much land for commercial exploitation but has in the process _____ the communities that lived there. Rich argues that centralized development cannot _____ the problems of the developing world in any effective way; he believes that a network of agencies should be _____ to _____ the task of funding suitable technologies for these societies.

bring about	put forward
deal with	set back
drive out	set up
open up	take on

**1.19
TASK**

Find words or phrases in 'The World Bank – a world threat?' which mean the following:

Paragraph 1: A representative of a country or an organization
Paragraph 2: A leading partner in a questionable activity
Paragraph 3: Requiring more investment in equipment than in labour
Policy imposed by senior managers
Destroyed
Paragraph 4: Geared to making few changes to the environment
Easy to approach or contact

1.20

Japan has the highest score on the Human Development Index. How has technology helped it to achieve a higher score in the three areas which make up this measurement?

■ GDP per head

■ Adult literacy

■ Life expectancy

1.21 | # Key Vocabulary

access to…	hazardous
accomplice	implementation
acid rain	incentive
agenda	indigenous
aggressive	(gross) national product
beneficiary	overuse
capital-intensive	ozone layer
cash crop	permit
CO_2 (carbon dioxide)	pesticide
critical issue	pollution
deforestation	to press ahead
desertification	prime
to devastate	productivity
developed	radical
developing/ (less) developed countries	sustainable development
to displace	top-down
to evolve	tradeable
to exploit	to trade on
global warming	transboundary
greenhouse effect	unwitting

Fuel, power and natural resources

When you have finished this chapter you should be able to

■ understand and take part in discussions about how natural resources are used and managed

■ express your own views on the need to balance higher standards of living with threats to the human and animal population

■ understand and use a range of terms employed in specialist discussions of these matters

2.1

Warm-up

When should environmental concerns give way to improving the quality of human life?

Are engineering projects (such as dams) that are designed to relieve problems such as drought bound to harm wildlife?

Will science eventually provide us with perfectly clean and unharmful power sources, or should we scale down our needs?

2.2

The recorded discussion focuses on the possible connection between electrical power lines and the incidence of cancer.

Note these key words and phrases:

to brew	to contest
epidemiological	to shield
susceptible to	to construe... as...
leuk(a)emia	sociological
control group	socioeconomic
exposure to...	substation
magnetic field	traffic density

2.3
TASK

Complete the following sentences:

1   A study carried out in Colorado in 1979 indicated that...
2   The 1979 study was contested because...
3   It is difficult to draw conclusions from most of the studies, because...
4   The socioeconomic position of people living near power lines could also be significant, as...
5   Because many power lines follow traffic routes, ...

2.4

How could the socioeconomic position of the people described in the recording expose them to a greater threat of developing cancer? Have there been any such cases in your country? Do the people accept this risk as a price that has to be paid for modern living?

2.5

The recorded discussion of how magnetic and electrical fields affect human tissues continues. The diagram below will help you to follow the discussion.

Note these key words and phrases:

to establish a link   manipulation
cell   simultaneous
laboratory   variation
(mechanical) stresses   to infer
background   ultimately

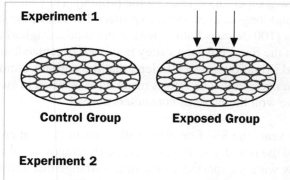

Experiment 1

One sample is exposed to a magnetic field, the other is not. Any changes, over a period of time m, in the DNA of the control group are compared to changes in the exposed group.

Control Group   **Exposed Group**

Experiment 2

Neither sample is exposed. Changes in the DNA of the two groups over time T are noted and compared. The difference between these two samples is then compared to the difference between the samples in the first experiment.

Control Group 1   **Control Group 2**

2.6
TASK

Complete the following sentences:

1 Background factors have to be eliminated from experiments...

2 Because the effects in such experiments are likely to be small,...

3 It is difficult to establish any link between magnetic fields and increased cancer incidence, because...

4 Sometimes more than one control group has to be set up...

2.7
TEXT

What benefits can advanced agricultural techniques bring to hot and traditionally drought-ridden areas?

A breadbasket in the backlands

The men gazed intently as the dog chased the whirlwind. Such an event is taken as a bad omen in the drought-stricken backlands of northeastern Brazil. However, Roque Cagliari doesn't worry. He is the general manager of the Garibaldina vineyard in Santa María da Boa Vista, in the state of Pernambuco. Weather forecasts indicate that this summer will be a dry season, which is good for the grapes; they will be able to ripen properly in the vineyards irrigated by the São Francisco river.

The workers leave superstition and resume pruning. They all wear wide-brimmed hats and long-sleeved shirts to protect them from the sun. It is 37 degrees Celsius (100 degrees Fahrenheit) in the shade. Cagliari explains that fruit farming in the São Francisco valley is so well organized, and systems of fertilization and irrigation are so efficient, that the region's almost permanent drought is quite irrelevant. The efforts made have resulted in sweeter, juicier grapes that have won the favor of consumers abroad.

In the past few years the São Francisco valley has made fruit crops a pillar of development of the hot, dry scrublands. Not only grapes but also mangoes and melons are now widely exported. Some find it strange that savory grapes can grow in the barren northeastern backlands; in Brazil, viniculture is usually associated with cooler, more humid southern climates. Nonetheless, in Santa Maria da Boa Vista, one of the best Brazilian wines, Botticelli, is produced in the Milano vineyard. The São Francisco valley bids fair to soon become a Brazilian California.

The success of fruit farming in this arid region is partly due to growing air and sea transport connecting the Brazilian northeast with Europe and the USA. However, the chief factor has been the combination of warm weather and irrigation. High temperatures and low humidity levels make fruits sweeter and richer. On the other hand, irrigation and fertilization compensate for the dryness and lack of soil nutrients and make more frequent harvests possible (two and a half a year, in the case of grapes). 'The São Francisco is pure gold. It provides all the water we need. Normal rainfall would be a liability,' says Cagliari.

Lena Castellón, Icaro (VARIG inflight magazine)

**2.8
TASK**

In which paragraphs of 'A breadbasket in the backlands' can you find the following? How is each item phrased?

1 Two fruits that are exported as well as grapes
2 The importance of the river to the farmers
3 Two factors that increase the sweetness and richness of fruits
4 The source of the vineyard's irrigation
5 What the vineyard workers are doing

**2.9
TASK**

Rewrite these sentences as shown in the example:

Example: He's a man **who uses his left hand**.
            *He's a **left-handed man**.*

1 He has a wife **who was born in Canada**.
2 Many cars are now assembled by robots **that have a remote control.**
3 He heard a scream **that curdled his blood.**
4 He has a girlfriend **who speaks French.**
5 Only cars **that have a full guarantee** are sold here.
6 This is a job **that needs two men.**

**2.10
TASK**

Complete the compound adjectives in the following sentences with the words in the box below:

Example: He had a _____-sharp mind and a good sense of humour.
            *He had a **razor-sharp** mind and a good sense of humour.*

1 She had to walk down a _____-black alleyway to reach the house.
2 They found out that the burglers had got through a _____-open window.
3 You can swim in _____-clear waters in the West Indies.
4 The glue set _____-hard within minutes.
5 She bought him a _____-gold watch for his birthday.

crystal	pitch	solid
razor	rock	wide

2.11

Imagine that you are a farmer in the São Francisco valley. What hopes or fears do you have for the future of your area? How viable do you feel the project is in the long-term?

2.12
TEXT

Who should make decisions affecting human and animal environments?

Dam scheme threatens Spain's bird life

The European Commission is considering funding a vast development scheme in Spain which, critics claim, would seriously damage nearly 50 bird areas protected under European law. The plan, which would cost hundreds of billions of pesetas to implement, involves building dams, roads, flood defence works, oil pipelines, irrigation schemes and electric power lines to modernise the country's water and energy supplies and transport network. Its sheer scale has shocked environmentalists, who claim it is 'ecologically nonsensical'.

The most controversial part of the scheme involves building 63 dams and 38 canals, tapping some of Spain's rivers to irrigate farmland in the rain-starved south. One project, the Monteagudo dam, would flood 3,000 hectares of woods and grassland, home to a large population of black storks and Spanish imperial eagles.

Conservationists say it is pointless spending money to increase production of crops already in oversupply. Irrigation projects on the river Guadalquivir have already damaged the river's delta, one of the most important wildlife sanctuaries in southern Europe. More than half of Europe's bird species can be found here, but numbers are dwindling as the water table drops.

The Spanish government claims the country needs the dams to solve its drought problem. Rainfall on the plains is sparse and rationing common. EU money would also be used to prepare for the 1995 World Alpine Skiing Championships in the Sierra Nevada and to extend a wind farm at Tarifa. The farm, consisting of 300 turbines, lies in the path of 300,000 migrating birds which fly to Africa every autumn. Hundreds have already been killed by the rotating blades. The owners now want to build an extra 1,700 turbines.

Environmentalists complain that the development plan disregards the protection areas designated under the 1979 EC Birds Directive and ignores the Habitats Directive protecting wildlife areas and endangered species. Neither does it have the support of the farmers it is supposed to benefit. On the dry Spanish steppes, where irrigation would devastate rare bird habitats, many farmers are paid for managing the land in a traditional way.

The European

D·A·M·N·A·T·I·O·N?

2.13
TASK

Complete the following sentences:

1 The irrigation project is something of a paradox, because…
2 The main effect of extending the Tarifa wind farm, according to environmentalists, will be…
3 The farmers whom the project was set up to help have…
4 Conservationists take the view that the irrigation project…
5 If the European Commission is really serious about protecting wildlife and endangered species, it…

2.14
ROLE PLAY

The irrigation of the São Francisco valley has caused damage of the type described in 'Dam scheme threatens Spain's bird life'. A local politician (Role **A** – page 122) and an environmentalist (Role **B** – page 124) argue over the future of the project.

2.15
TASK

Combine each of the following sentences with one from the box below, using **where**, **which** *or* **who** *to make one sentence:*

Example: The wind farm consists of 300 turbines.
The wind farm, **which lies in the path of migrating birds**, *consists of 300 turbines.*

1 The delta of the river Guadalquivir has been damaged by irrigation projects.
2 Environmentalists claim the plan is 'ecologically nonsensical'.
3 The plan involves building dams, roads, flood defence works and oil pipelines.
4 The European Commission is considering funding a vast dam scheme in Spain.
5 EU money would be used to prepare the Sierra Nevada ski area.

> It would cost hundreds of billions of pesetas to implement.
> They are shocked by the sheer scale of it.
> The 1995 World Championships are being held there.
> More than half of Europe's bird species can be found there.
> It is based in Brussels.
> **It lies in the path of migrating birds.**

2.16
TASK

Make sentences by matching each person on the left with a correct phrase on the right. Supply the correct word for the two phrases that are left:

1 a paleozoologist
2 an entomologist
3 a seismologist
4 an astrophysicist
5 a pathologist
6 a meteorologist
7 a _____
8 an _____

is interested in stars and related phenomena
studies the weather
is concerned with telepathy and clairvoyance
performs post-mortems on dead bodies
examines fossilized animals
studies insects
is interested in and studies birds
is an expert on earthquakes

**2.17
TASK**

Between 1988 and 1992, the German chemicals firm Bayer AG spent DM611 million on air pollution control measures, equipping power plants with low-emission catalyst processes and installing gas purification units.

Study the chart below, then use it to make a presentation to the board of Bayer on the results of the initiative.

Air emissions at Bayer AG:

Significant reductions since 1988

Component	1988	1989	1990	1991	1992	1993†
Dust emissions	1,200	1,100	920	920	900	750
Sulphur dioxide	15,900	13,200	10,300	9,400	8,000	6,000
Nitrogen oxides*	12,500	10,900	8,200	7,800	7,200	5,700
Carbon monoxide	9,200	6,800	8,200	8,200	8,300	8,400
Org. compounds	1,900	1,700	1,300	1,300	1,300	1,300

*calculated as NO_2 †projected

2.18

Find a newspaper report or magazine article that deals with an environmental or natural resource problem in your country or region. Summarize it and be able to answer questions about it.

2.19 Key Vocabulary

arid	manipulation
backland	to migrate
to brew	nonsensical
cancer	nutrient
to construe... as...	omen
to contest	a pillar of...
control group	pointless
controversial	to ration
to designate	sanctuary
drought (-stricken)	to shield
to dwindle	simultaneous
ecological	socioeconomic
to establish a link	sociological
exposure to...	(mechanical) stress
humid	substation
to infer	susceptible to
irrelevant	to tap
to irrigate/irrigation	traffic density
laboratory	ultimate(ly)
leukemia (Am)/ leukaemia (Br)	variation
	viniculture
liability	whirlwind

3

Using technology

When you have finished this chapter you should be able to

- understand and take part in discussions of how technology affects people – and how people's needs and characteristics affect technology

- express your own views on the difficulties, opportunities and dangers underlying the applications of technology

- understand and use a range of terms employed in specialist discussions of these matters

3.1

Warm-up

"Technology is neutral, what people do with it is either good or bad." Think of examples which support this statement and some which rebut it.

Should the solutions to problems which are created by technology involve even more technology or less?

3.2

In the recording a specialist discusses innovations in the field of bar codes. The bar codes on page 23 will help you to follow the discussion.

Note these key words and phrases:

bar code	licence*(Br)*/license*(Am)* plate
retail area/sector	two-dimensional
linear	character
checkout	drum
datafile	pallet

3.3
TASK

Complete the following sentences:

1 At present, bar codes are mostly seen...
2 When shoppers arrive at the checkout,...
3 Linear bar codes are like licence plates: ...
4 Two-dimensional bar codes will be able to...
5 A 'portable datafile' is useful because...
6 Dealing with poisonous material will be made easier...
7 Problems encountered in shipping goods from one place to another...

A can of beans

5 000157 001719 >

The one-dimensional bar code we see in the supermarket can only be understood if it is read into a data file on a computer.

The United Nations Charter

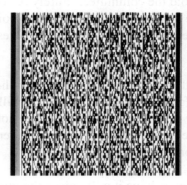

This two-dimensional bar code contains all the relevant information within it. There is no need for a separate data file.

3.4 How do you think two-dimensional bar codes could be introduced to the following areas?

- the movement of hazardous waste
- drivers' licences
- supermarket goods
- drugs/medicine

How can today's more sophisticated technologies minimize the adverse effects of an older technology on communities – for example, its use by criminals?

A smart gun knows its owner

A gun that will only fire when held by its designated user is being developed in a joint project between the US Department of Justice and the Pentagon.

Such a 'smart' gun could prove a boon, especially to police officers and children. One in four officers killed in the US is shot with his or her own gun, according to David Boyd, director of science and technology at the National Institute of Justice. But prisoners would not be able to shoot a smart 'safe' gun even if they managed to steal one from an officer.

America's police are still equipped 'much as Wyatt Earp in the late 19th century', Boyd told the committee. 'Surely America's sophisticated technology base can provide better alternatives.' He also pointed out that every year hundreds of American children shoot themselves while playing with a parent's gun.

The safe gun will be designed with sensors in the handle to monitor who is gripping it. If it fails to recognise the grip, it will not fire. Because the project is still in its very early stages, designers have not decided on the best method of identifying the user – whether by pressure, temperature, palm print or fingerprint, or some combination of these.

The gun's developers hope it will reduce the misuse of firearms, which are fast becoming the prime form of unnatural death in the US. 'We know technology can't fix every shortcoming. We know it can't make up for poor judgment or compensate for inadequate or nonexistent training,' admits Boyd. But it can make police and public safer and the police more efficient, he says.

Vincent Kiernan, New Scientist

**3.6
ANALYSIS**

1 What views do you have on the use of firearms by police officers? Does the text reassure you or make you more apprehensive?

2 What conclusions do you draw from the fact that so many American police officers are shot with their own guns?

3 Which would be the best method of identifying the user of a safe gun – by pressure, temperature or fingerprint?

4 What other methods have you heard of for uniquely identifying people, for instance for security purposes?

**3.7
TASK**

Technology which allows only a designated user to operate something could be applied elsewhere. For each of the following examples, state whether such technology would be:

Feasible   *Desirable*

- cars

- medicine bottles

- nuclear warheads

- computer software

3.8

David Boyd states here that technology cannot 'make up for poor judgment or compensate for inadequate or nonexistent training.' What implications does this statement have for modern society, in your view? Do you think that education in the uses and abuses of technology should be given a higher priority?

3.9
TEXT

Many technological developments, such as airports and power stations, are criticized because they spoil the landscape. Is there a case for building such structures offshore – or even on a floating base?

Floating wind farm awaits fans

A tiny wind turbine in a test tank at Teddington, Middlesex (England) could hold the key to wind power's most difficult public relations problem: making this form of renewable energy environmentally acceptable to all. The model turbine, standing around three metres high, was developed as the first part of a three-stage research programme called FLOAT. The first stage cost £750,000, half of which was financed by the UK Government's Department of Trade and Industry.

Floating on a hollow concrete hull, the turbine would be moored to anchors by polyester ropes designed to keep it stable even in hurricane-force winds. An undersea cable would feed the power ashore into Britain's National Grid.

Tests to assess the project's environmental impact, design requirements and economics have now been completed successfully, yet its future still hangs in the balance. Between £2 million and £3 million is needed to finance Stage 2 of the programme, which involves building a prototype offshore turbine. 'We are looking towards EC funding,' says Koon Tong, a naval architect with Technomare, the London offshore engineering company that is leading a consortium set up to develop the turbine. 'Department of Trade and Industry sources for research and development seem to be drying up.'

In the 1970s and 1980s, environmentalists saw wind power as an ideal energy source. It does not produce noxious pollutants or add to the greenhouse effect, and it helps to reduce dependence on nuclear power. Its most enduring image was an idealised country scene with a windmill.

Since 1991, when the government started to subsidize alternatives to fossil fuel, nearly two dozen wind farms have been opened in Britain. But the reality of rows of turbines standing on high ground, visible for miles, has split environmentalists into those who support renewable energy in any form and those who want to avoid what they see as desecration of the countryside.

Though offshore structures are expensive, floating wind farms have advantages over their land-based relatives. The consortium points out that turbine speeds on land have to be limited to minimise noise, and that wind flow over water is more constant.

Mick Hamer, New Scientist

26

3.10
TASK

Complete the following sentences:

1   The stability of an offshore wind turbine can...
2   The advantages of wind power as an energy source are...
3   Some environmentalists have opposed wind turbine development...
4   The floating wind farm has the advantages of...
5   Building large numbers of floating wind farms could...

3.11
TASK

Each of the following titles has two different meanings. Look at the words in boldface type and explain the two meanings:

1   'Floating wind farm awaits **fans**.'
2   'The factory workers are **idle**.'
3   'Ford have made two new **models** this year.'
4   'There's no **concrete** evidence.'
5   'A smart gun should prove a **boon** to police officers.'
6   'The Swedes drive on the **right** side of the road.'

3.12
TASK

Rewrite these sentences, leaving out any words that are not necessary and making any other changes:

Example: The model turbine, which stands at an
                approximate height of three metres...
                *The model turbine, **standing around three
                metres high**...*

1   The turbine floats on a hollow hull made of concrete and would be moored to anchors by ropes made of polyester.
2   A vision of rows of turbines which stand on high ground and which are visible for miles has split environmentalist opinion.
3   Stage 2 of the programme, which involves building a prototype offshore turbine, will cost up to £3 million.
4   Although offshore wind farms are expensive, they have advantages over land-based farms.
5   A gun that will only fire when a designated user is holding it is now being developed.

3.13

"Environmentalism is a general term for complaints about technology." Discuss.

3.14
TEXT

Given the security threat to electronic communications systems, why does the accessibility of technology remain a prime goal of researchers?

Tools that empower people

Imagine being lost on a mountain. You know there's a path to the road, but all you can see are hills, lakes and woods, and the map you brought along is little more than a sketch. This is the moment that you need the device so beloved of 1950s science fiction – a communicator. A small device that can display detailed maps of the area, send messages to the emergency services and, if you've got the advanced model, beam you back home.

Well, there's a small group of scientists working in a California development laboratory who'd like to help you out. The communicator may not beam you home yet, but General Magic, founded in 1990 by Mark Porat, Bill Atkinson and Andy Herzfeld, is already making the future of personal communications happen.

Atkinson says: 'My drive is to produce tools that empower people.' That is why General Magic spends so much time developing a computer environment known as Magic Cap, which will one day make hand-held personal communicators cosy to use in a tight spot. This piece of software provides both the graphics that the user sees and various software hooks for connecting different interface devices and services.

The interface uses familiar images to show the services available, such as address lists, electronic mail and reference material. What you see when you switch on the machine is a desk with images of office items like a phone, notepad and a postcard. Want to send a message? Just tap on the postcard and a blank card appears ready for addressing. Itching to play a game? Then touch the word 'hallway' in the top right of the screen and pick the door that says 'games room'. Need more services? Just move 'downtown' and pick the building offering the service you want.

General Magic gauges the usability of its devices by inviting people into the laboratory to try them out. David Leffler, who monitors their performance hidden behind a one-way mirror, says it can be frustrating for development engineers to watch users stumble over their interfaces. But the developers can respond to criticism almost immediately; it can take less than twenty minutes to revise an image rejected by a user.

Netropolis supplement, New Scientist

3.15 TASK

In which paragraph of 'Tools that empower people' do you find the following information? How is it expressed in the text?

1 The images that appear on the screen when the machine is turned on
2 That 'guinea pigs' are used to test the devices
3 Who started General Magic and when
4 That the 'communicator' was favoured by 1950s sci-fi books and films
5 That various services can be connected by means of software.

3.16 TASK

Rewrite the following euphemistic sentences, using simple and direct words or phrases:

Example: Euphemistic language: *The map you brought along is little more than a sketch.*
More direct language: *The map you brought along is **almost useless.***

1 The shoes he was wearing had seen better days.
2 He's not as slim and fit as he used to be.
3 The Cabinet Minister was economical with the truth.
4 I'd like to buy the Ferrari, but it's beyond my resources at the moment.
5 Three men were expelled from the country yesterday for activities detrimental to national security.
6 'You might feel a little discomfort,' said the dentist.
7 The estate agent's details said that the house was in need of some attention.
8 If you don't pay me what you owe me, I'll start proceedings against you.

3.17

Think of as many advantages as possible of using an electronic notebook instead of a traditional paper-based one. Summarize your findings and be ready to answer questions on them.

3.18 | # Key Vocabulary

bar code	linear
boon	to monitor
character	to moor
checkout	noxious
to compensate for	offshore
consortium	pallet
cosy	palm print
datafile	pollutant
to dry up	polyester
emergency services	prototype
enduring	renewable
fingerprint	retail area/sector
fossil fuel	sensor
frustrating	shortcoming
to gauge	smart (e.g. smart card)
graphics	to subsidize
hurricane-force winds	turbine
idealised	two-dimensional
interface	undersea
licence (Br)/license (Am) plate	

The world of IT systems

When you have finished this chapter you should be able to

- understand and take part in discussions about the uses of information technology

- express your own views on the applications of single-chip systems – cellular phones, fax machines and the like – in business and everyday life

- understand and use a range of terms employed in specialist discussions of these matters

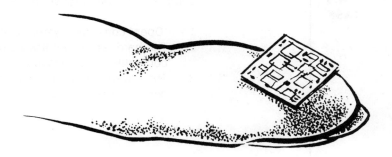

4.1

Warm-up

What benefits result from the miniaturization and customization of information systems hardware? Are business and professions ready to take advantage of these benefits?

Can organizations deal with the opportunities and threats presented by global communications networks?

4.2

In the recording a consultant talks about the more competitive computer hardware and software markets that have grown up over the past decade, and the development of "open" systems.

Note these key words and phrases:

cost/time penalties	performance curve (price
hardware	curve, functionality curve)
software	to mushroom
vendor	to mature
proprietory	functionality
environment	flexibility (of purchase)

4.3
TASK

Complete the following sentences:

1   'Open' computer systems allow users to...
2   The hardware and software markets are now more competitive in... because...
3   The advantage of 'flexibility of purchase' for the consumer is that...

4.4

What evidence of "open"-ness and flexibility have you come across in the computer systems you have used?

How have makers of electronic products been affected by
advances in system design over the years?

Seeking the one-chip system

Makers of electronic gear have long sought one-chip systems to lower costs,
boost performance and personalize products. Since the invention of the
microprocessor in 1971, a series of technical innovations have brought us
closer to all-in-one systems.

1971 Microprocessor invented by Intel with 2,700 transistors.
Made possible one-chip watches and calculators.

1975 Emergence of microcontrollers, special microprocessors
with added circuitry tailored for specific jobs.

1982 Rise of application-specific integrated circuits (ASICs)
Manufacturers merge more peripheral circuitry onto
fewer logic chips that work with the microprocessor.
This reduces the number of devices in products,
leading to (among other things) cheaper photocopiers.

1993 Chip-design tools emerge that can customize
microprocessors – combining memory, ASIC modules
and other circuitry with a fast processor 'core' of a
million or more transistors. By linking software-
generated models of these elements, product designers
mix and match to create one-chip systems.

1999 Better design tools, chips of 50 million to 100 million
transistors, and a growing library of circuit modules
will let product designers crank out advanced systems-
on-a-chip, including mainframe-class personal digital
assistants.

4.6
TASK

Rewrite the following, using the words given:

Example: 1971: Microprocessors invented by Intel. Made possible one-chip watches and calculators.
WERE MADE/IN 1971/INTEL'S INVENTION
*One-chip watches and calculators **were made** possible **in 1971** by **Intel's invention** of micro-processors.*

1   1975: Emergence of microcontrollers.
EMERGED/MID-

2   1982: Rise of application-specific integrated circuits.
USE/ASICS/ROSE

3   1993: Chip-design tools emerge that can customize high-end microprocessors.
THAT WERE CAPABLE/IN 1993

4   1999: Better design tools and chips of 50 million to 100 million transistors will let product designers crank out systems-on-a-chip.
IT IS PREDICTED THAT/OF BETWEEN 50 AND/ALLOW

4.7
TASK

Listed below are five consumer electronic goods which have become smaller since first coming on the market. Rank them 1 - 5 in terms of their improvements since their introduction in each of the three areas:

	Performance (speed, reliability)	Functionality	Price
personal stereo			
video recorder			
calculators			
cellular phones			
electronic personal organizers			

Which ones still have the most potential for improvement?

Do computerization and networking make an organization
more vulnerable to criminal activity?

Robbery on the information highway?

The Internet global communications network offers an international medium
of contact, conference and collaboration, available to anyone who can access
an attached computer terminal. Its appeal is wide, extending far beyond the
ranks of academic and business computer enthusiasts: in Seattle, in the US
Northwest, a number of homeless library users have become regular Internet
'surfers'. Yet the established norms of electronic cooperation on which the
network depends are already under threat.

The Internet system is made up of some 2.5 million attached computers and
30,000 interconnected networks. These elements exchange massive amounts
of information on the basis of a mere electronic handshake between users. The
system therefore relies on a large measure of mutual trust, tolerance and
respect – and it is this very dependence that makes it vulnerable.

Network users are well aware that electronic-mail messages may be read by
people other than the intended recipients. A less well-known fact is that e-mail
and other networked communications can be easily and untraceably forged:
there is no guarantee that any message received over the net has come from the
stated sender. This means that an electronic impersonator pretending to be a
trusted colleague of another system user can persuade that person to reveal
confidential information. E-mail messages, appropriately coded, can trigger
electronic responses that will open all the recipient's files to the sender.
Professional secrecy and loyalty can thus be undermined and illegal activities
solicited.

It is difficult, even for those using the Internet every day, to appreciate the
scale of the threat to security. Groups of corporate network users, accessing
freely shared data from file servers, are usually accustomed to regarding their
own organizational boundaries as the accepted limit of their electronic activity.
But when these private and trusting environments are opened up to access
through the Internet, virtually any file on any computer is a potential victim of
electronic trickery. And the more computers and computer networks there are
in an organization, the greater the risk of attack.

4.9
TASK

Complete the following sentences:

1   E-mail cannot be considered wholly reliable because...
2   Users of systems such as the Internet have depended up to now on...
3   Electronic impersonation is a way of...
4   If system users cannot be sure that a message on their computers is a genuine one, they...
5   The Internet has a wide appeal which...

4.10

Most network users are adamantly opposed to any form of government regulation of the Internet. As criminal activity increases, will it become necessary to police the Internet? Is such an undertaking feasible?

**4.11
TASK**

Explain the difference in meaning between these pairs of sentences:

1   (a) He couldn't even use the computer.
        (b) Even he couldn't use the computer.

2   (a) She even learned to swim on holiday.
        (b) Even she learned to swim on holiday.

3   (a) He even remembered her name.
        (b) Even he remembered her name.

**4.12
TASK**

Rewrite the following sentences, adding an appropriate clause from the box below:

Example: It is difficult to appreciate the scale of the threat to security.
                *It is difficult, **even for those using the Internet every day**, to appreciate the scale of the threat to security.*

1   It is difficult to estimate the needs of network users.
2   It is not easy to give up smoking.
3   It is possible to learn a foreign language.
4   It is easy to drive an automatic car.
5   It is impossible to run as fast as a cheetah.
6   It is a challenge to forecast the growth of one-chip systems.

> specialists in electronics
> the most determined
> the highly computer-literate
> the very athletic
> people with poor memories
> the most uncoordinated
> ***those using the Internet every day***

4.13

In the recording, the discussion of open systems and consumer choice raises the issues of price, diversity and performance.

Note these key words and phrases:

analogy
to escalate, escalation
astronomical(ly)
bottom line
confrontation
(un)ambiguous

a reverse trend
rationalization
cartel
diversity
to come into play
convergence

4.14
ANALYSIS

1   Why is there less choice in the computer hardware market than in software?
2   Which factor is expected to stimulate creativity in the hardware market?
3   What will be the likely effect of competition on chip technology?

4.15
TASK

The speaker on the tape says: 'Customers don't buy chips, they buy solutions.' Assess yourself as a product buyer or a solution buyer. List some products that you have bought over the past one or two years, either for your home or your business. Rank on a scale of 1 (no knowledge) to 5 (full knowledge) the level of technical understanding that you brought to each purchase. Then give yourself an overall assessment.

Product   *Your ranking*

_____   _____

_____   _____

_____   _____

_____   _____

_____   _____

4.16
TASK

Imagine that you are working in a university research institute. One Monday, you and your colleagues receive a memorandum from the head of the institute. Read the excerpt below, then finish the memo by listing the necessary procedures and safeguards.

MEMORANDUM

c.c.

Finance Staff

We have reason to believe that hackers or electronic pirates attempted to access the files on our network on Thursday or Friday, 25-26 June. In the same week, electronic impersonation took place on the e-mail system, leading some system users to reveal confidential information.

It is impossible to exaggerate the seriousness of this situation. It is vitally important to safeguard the security of our system files. Therefore, until further notice, all system users must ensure that the following procedures are carried out:

4.17

Which issues addressed in this chapter are most significant for business systems and communication? Rank the following in order of their importance to you, and be prepared to explain your selection in a brief presentation.

1   Improvements in systems-on-a-chip, including personal digital assistants.
2   The growth of open systems and flexible purchasing options for computer users.
3   Price wars fought by chip manufacturers.
4   The vulnerability of computer files in global communications systems such as the Internet.
5   The possibility of electronic impersonation in e-mail facilities.

4.18

Present as many arguments as possible for not having an e-mail facility on a wide area network.

4.19 | # Key Vocabulary

to access	impersonator
all-in-one system	to mature
(un)ambiguous	microprocessor
analogy	to mix and match
application	to mushroom
astronomical(ly)	norm
bottom line	one-chip system
cartel	(cost) penalties
cellular phone	performance curve
circuitry	price curve
	functionality curve
to come into play	peripheral
computer terminal	rationalization
confrontation	recipient
convergence	
diversity	a reverse trend
electronic mail, e-mail	software
to escalate, escalation	to tailor
flexibility (of purchase)	(un)traceable
functionality	to undermine
global communications	vendor
hardware	vulnerable

Technology and everyday life

When you have finished this chapter you should be able to

■ understand and take part in discussions about the impact of contemporary technology on everyday life

■ explain and express your own views on how information technology affects the quality of human life

■ understand and use a range of terms employed in specialist discussions of these matters

5.1

Warm-up

What is the educational system in your country doing to keep up with and make use of the latest innovations in technology?

Are you aware of the role of digital technology in improving the appliances and systems that you use in everyday life?
Should you be?

What does the term 'multimedia' mean to you?

5.2

In the recording a marketing manager from Hewlett Packard comments on the projected uses of electronic technology in the home. But won't bringing this to the home involve more expense and equipment than the average householder can afford?

Note these key words and phrases:

bandwidth	to figure out
channel	cost-effective
to dial up	demographics
box of tricks	hype
High Street *(Br)/*	like wildfire
Main Street *(Am)*	to tarmac, tarmacking
roughly	

**5.3
TASK**

Complete the following sentences:

1   Higher bandwidths make it possible to...
2   Investment in the new technologies may fail...
3   The uses of electronic technologies today can be compared...
4   The growth of the information superhighway will...

5.4

The speaker on the recording says: 'There will be some applications which will really take off like wildfire.' Which applications of information technology are likely to be most successful?

**5.5
TASK**

Below is a list of technological innovations which failed to materialize for years after they were initially promised. For each case come up with possible reasons why.

- home shopping
- video telephones
- high definition television
- robots in the home
- digital audio tape (DAT)

ROBBIE THE ROBOT

How can the traditional school curriculum be made relevant to the demands of the electronic age and the global village?

School's out...

Somewhere on the West Coast of America, five children are kicking around ideas for the design of an Antarctic research station. Their talk is peppered with references to prototypes produced on their PCs, e-mail from scientists on site, and jokes about a video conference with a potential backer for the project.

This is not the opening gambit from some Hollywood 'kids-outsmart-the-grown-ups' movie, but video footage of a real maths lesson for teenagers devised by educationists in California. And it's part of a movement that is gaining ground in both classroom and boardroom as America comes to terms with the implications of the information revolution. Enthusiasts say that old-style pedagogy will teach the wrong skills in a future where people will work in groups brought together for the lifetime of a particular project, where they will constantly have to learn new skills, and where the traditional corporation, with its rigid hierarchical structure, will have lost ground to companies that dare to bring in more complex, self-governing management styles.

The Antarctica Project has brought together staff from Stanford University, teachers from the San Francisco Bay area and researchers from the Institute for Research on Learning (IRL), a non-profit-making organization based in Palo Alto and founded by Xerox in 1987 to 'rethink learning'. Almost without knowing it, the children are absorbing the basic principles of geometry and algebra as they work in much the same way as the professional engineers, architects and scientists they are mimicking – and even consulting from time to time.

This is all a far cry from the 'hard-tech' vision of future education being pushed by the makers of CD-ROM encyclopedias and the enthusiasts for interactive TV. These people see our children and grandchildren glued to their computers, learning more and faster because their textbooks are souped up with graphics, songs and video clips, or watching lessons-on-demand TV that beams the media stars from the teaching profession right into their living rooms. But 'wiring up the kids' is dismissed by Ted Kahn, a consultant at IRL. Education, he says, must be more than a means of pouring knowledge into children's heads: it needs to recognise the way people learn.

'Netropolis' supplement, New Scientist'

5.7 TASK

Which aspects of this method of teaching reflect a new understanding of the way people learn and which aspects are geared to helping the children to get jobs?

How people learn   **Getting jobs**

5.8 TASK

Make adjectives from the nouns in the box by adding a similar suffix each time (and making any other necessary spelling changes). Then put the correct adjectives in the sentences below:

pedagogy	technology
hierarchy	practice
geometry	crisis
theory	

Example: Computer-assisted design software enables users to create complex _____ patterns on the screen.
Computer-assisted design software enables users to create complex geometric patterns on the screen.

1   The speed of _____ innovation will require us all to learn new skills.
2   Many think that traditional _____ management structures will give way to more open, self-governing styles.
3   What used to be thought of as the _____ convergence of computing, telecommunications and video is now a reality.
4   Will _____ considerations of cost restrict the growth of IT in the home?
5   The cost of new product development is a _____ issue for chip manufacturers.
6   Some people think that old-style _____ practices teach the wrong skills for the future.

5.9
TEXT

What new opportunities does interactive television offer to viewers?

Open television: expanding consumer choice

Nicholas Negroponte of the Massachusetts Institute of Technology's innovative Media Laboratory is a pioneer of 'open' information technologies. The 'multimedia' revolution in IT began in 1975, when he first used that term to refer to the product of the convergence of telecommunications, computing and video.

Today, Negroponte's work is focused on another conceptual leap forward, based on the use of digitally-based data for everyday information delivery. He foresees the development of home-based 'intelligent' IT systems which will not only manage future household tasks more efficiently – answering the phone, re-ordering groceries and other supplies and sorting incoming electronic mail – but will also enable consumers to improve the technical quality of the information they receive and even to edit it to suit their tastes.

The exploitation of such 'open television' systems is facilitated by the use of digital information rather than the analogue signals traditionally employed in TV broadcasting. Users will view news bulletins, presented in a customized edited form, when they want to. They will be able to view their favourite movies at selected convenient times; the films will be delivered down a telephone line when they are required. Interactive TV will make it possible for viewers to change the shape of programmes, choosing from alternative endings or deleting inappropriate material. Such innovations will not only put traditionally passive viewers in control of what they see and when they see it; they will also put intelligence into the ordinary domestic TV, which Negroponte regards as 'per cubic inch, the dumbest appliance in the home'.

Until now, most convergent developments in IT have been driven by business priorities. Behind Negroponte's vision lies a concern for improving the quality of everyday domestic life, providing a wider field of choice for consumers and a livelier competitive products market. He sees IT as a means of helping ordinary people to become the masters of the information they consume; convergent technologies, in his view, promise greater freedom.

**5.10
TASK**

Which of the following statements accurately reflect information from the text 'Open television: expanding consumer choice'? Select the items that apply:

❑ 1. The term 'multimedia' was coined in 1975 by Nicholas Negroponte.
❑ 2. Negroponte believes that IT systems will soon be used in the home to carry out everyday tasks.
❑ 3. With open television, viewers will be able to select what they watch and when they watch it.
❑ 4. Interactive TV will enable viewers to select but not alter television programmes.
❑ 5. Negroponte's current focus is on using convergent technologies to meet the needs of businesses.

**5.11
TASK**

Rewrite the following sentences without loss of meaning, using the words given:

Example: Films can be sent down a telephone line when they are needed. DELIVER/REQUIRE
*Films can be **delivered** down a telephone line when they are **required**.*

1   Digital information enables users to control and change the information they consume. OPPORTUNITY
2   Negroponte argues that today's TV set is the dumbest appliance in the home. ACCORDING TO/LEAST
3   Most convergent developments have so far been driven by business priorities rather than domestic needs. UP TO NOW/INFLUENCED MORE
4   Negroponte's vision of convergent technologies is to ensure that consumers will have the greatest freedom. CONCEPT/IS INTENDED TO GIVE
5   Open television will let viewers watch news bulletins when they want to. ENABLE/REQUIRE

5.12
TASK

Combine the two sentences using the gerund:

Example: Negroponte has a vision of the future.
It leads him to a world where intelligent TV systems deliver customized material.
Having a vision of the future *leads Negroponte to a world where intelligent TV systems deliver customized material.*

1   Julia forgot to record the TV programme.
It meant that she missed her favourite soap opera.
2   Consumers will be able to choose when they watch TV programmes.
This will enable them to control their own viewing patterns.
3   Viewers can interact with their televisions.
It means, for example, that they can change the ending of films.
4   Harry asked his boss for a pay increase.
It got him the sack.

5.13
TASK

Complete the following sentences, using the correct form of one of the three-part phrasal verbs in the box below:

1   The personal computer of the future will re-order your groceries before you _____ essentials.
2   Just when the industry thinks it has _____ new technology, researchers make another conceptual leap forward.
3   When you are busy, the home IT system of the future will handle your phone calls, letting you _____ your work.
4   With the advent of interactive TV, viewers can _____ more interesting evenings.
5   The possibility of editing TV programmes means that viewers will be able to _____ the points they don't enjoy.
6   Don't worry about your personal life; the 'intelligent' computer system will _____ household tasks.

take care of	run out of
catch up with	get on with
get rid of	look forward to

5.14

In the recording a specialist explains the use of object-based applications – that is, uses of IT systems based on entities in computer memory that contain related sets of information. How do objects bring the real world to computing?

Note these key words and phrases:

objects, object-based
programmer
procedural
to model

real-world entities
structural modularity
Lego ™
intuitive

**5.15
TASK**

Fill in each space with a word from the box below:

Traditionally, computer programmers have used _____ methods in program design, defining elements in high-level computer-based languages which are not _____ to human languages or _____ entities. In object-based applications, the emphasis is on the desired end result rather than on the processes _____ to reach such a result; in other words, the approach is practical and intuitive, focusing on real-world _____ in systems designed (say) to meet business needs. Software components can therefore be reused and _____ like pieces of Lego to create programs customized to the needs of the users.

elements
equipment
priorities
procedural

real-world
recombined
related
required

**5.16
TASK**

Imagine that you are working on a convergent technologies project similar to that described in 'Open television: expanding consumer choice' (page 46). Present a summary of your work to colleagues at a conference.

5.17

Find a list of local TV schedules and consider how you could edit the output and make it interactive. Explain your changes and be ready to answer questions.

5.18 | **Key Vocabulary**

analog *(Am)*/analogue *(Br)*	High Street *(Br)*/Main Street *(Am)*
backer	hype
bandwidth	interactive
boardroom	intuitive
box of tricks	to kick around ideas
channel	Lego ™
conceptual	maths *(Br)*/math *(Am)*
convergent	to mimic, mimicking
cost-effective	to model
demographics	multimedia
to dial up	objects, object-based
digital	passive
to edit	pedagogy
to facilitate	profit-making
a far cry from…	programmer
to figure out	procedural
footage	real-world entities
to gain/lose ground	structural modularity
(opening) gambit	to tarmac, tarmacking
hierarchical	like wildfire

6

Health issues

When you have finished this chapter you should be able to

■   understand and take part in discussions about
    contemporary health issues and medical research

■   express your own views on major health issues
    dangers and medical approaches

■   understand and use a range of terms employed in
    specialist discussions of these matters

<table>
<tr><td>

6.1

</td><td>

Warm-up

Is genetic research worth doing for its own sake or does it have to have a practical application?

Which threats to health arouse the greatest current public concern in your country, and what action can people take to respond to this concern?

Can today's cities still offer people a healthy living and working environment?

</td></tr>
</table>

6.2

In the recording a specialist in genetics talks about a project which attempts to map all the genes in the human genetic make-up. The diagram on the opposite page will help you follow the discussion.

Note these key words and phrases:

genome	chromosome
sequence	diagnostic
blueprint	genealogical
DNA (deoxyribonucleic acid)	predisposition
protein	cystic fibrosis
enzyme	mutation
catalyst	to correlate
organism	

**6.3
TASK**

Complete the following sentences:

1 The human genome project sets out to...
2 The genetic blueprint for the human organism is made up..., which...
3 Genetic researchers can carry out diagnostic work when they...
4 The genome research will be useful as a diagnostic tool because...
5 Some people argue that gene therapy is potentially harmful, as...

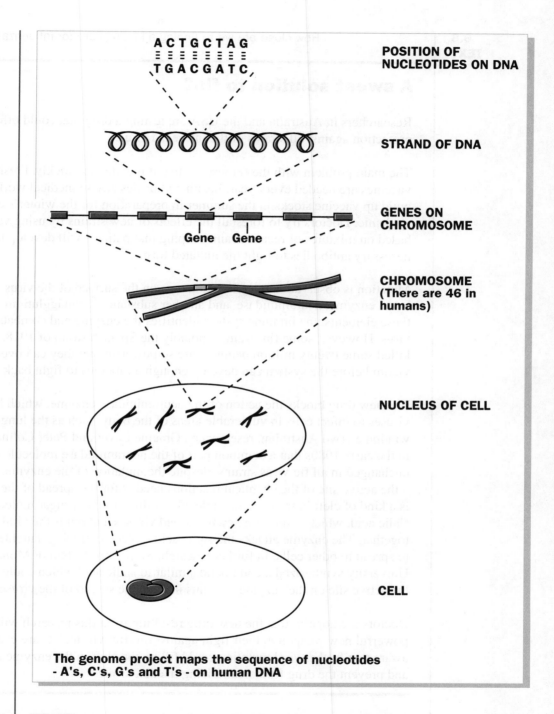

ACTGCTAG
TGACGATC

POSITION OF NUCLEOTIDES ON DNA

STRAND OF DNA

GENES ON CHROMOSOME

Gene   Gene

CHROMOSOME (There are 46 in humans)

NUCLEUS OF CELL

CELL

The genome project maps the sequence of nucleotides - A's, C's, G's and T's - on human DNA

6.4   How concerned are you that genetic researchers may attempt to breed specific characteristics in people?

How close are we to finding a lasting cure for influenza?

A sweet solution to flu?

Researchers in Australia and the USA are testing a drug that could offer protection against all strains of the influenza virus.

The main problem with the flu virus is that it mutates so quickly. Fresh vaccines are needed every year: health authorities advise medical workers to build up vaccine stocks in the summer in preparation for the winter's expected epidemic. Doctors try to forestall the effects of new strains by using vaccines based on mixtures of recent strains, hoping that patients will develop the necessary antibodies to fight the mutated forms.

Mutation is observable in 'spiky' elements on the surface of the virus, formed by an enzyme, neuraminidase, and another substance, hæmagglutinin. Meeting these elements, the immune system identifies the enzyme and combats the virus. However, some flu strains – notably the Spanish strain of 1918, which killed some twenty million people – are so powerful that they can overcome a victim before the system can develop enough antibodies to fight back.

The new drug blocks the action of the neuraminidase enzyme, which helps viruses to infect cells in vulnerable areas of the body, such as the lungs and the windpipe. Two Australian researchers, Graeme Laver and Peter Colman, found in the early 1980s that a common part of the neuraminidase molecule stayed unchanged in all flu virus strains, despite the mutation of the enzyme. This part – the active site of the chemical reactions needed for the spread of the virus – is a kind of cleft in the enzyme molecule, fitting around a sugar molecule, sialic acid, which resides on newly formed viruses and binds the viral elements together. The enzyme attacks the sialic acid molecule, freeing daughter viruses to spread to other cells. In further research, Mark von Itzstein of Monash University synthesized a compound similar to sialic acid which could block the active site on the enzyme and thus impede the spread of the viruses.

Doctors are hopeful that the new drug resulting from this research will be a powerful new weapon in their fight against flu. But virologists are cautious, aware that further viral mutation could fill up the cleft in the enzyme molecule and prevent the drug from neutralizing the active site.

6.6
TASK

Fill in each space wiith a word from the box below:

Influenza, or flu, is an acute _____ infection. Its main _____ are fever, fatigue, headache, pains in the joints and loss of _____ . Many cases of flu are quite mild, although often _____ enough to necessitate absence from work. Some attacks are much more _____, particularly if a _____ viral infection occurs. Influenza tends to come in waves because new _____ prove resistant to the body's _____ system and to _____ used against _____ forms of the disease.

appetite	severe
secondary	strains
immune	symptoms
previous	vaccines
serious	viral

6.7
TASK

Imagine that you are a researcher taking part in the project described in 'A sweet solution to flu?'. You are being interviewed by a journalist or a television presenter. Answer the following questions:

1   Why is it so hard to defeat the flu virus?
2   Why are you using a drug and not a vaccine?
3   Surely, most healthy individuals normally recover from flu, don't they?
4   How does the new drug prevent the virus from spreading?
5   Are you confident that the drug will provide a solution to flu epidemics?

6.8

Prepare a presentation for a news conference on the project described in 'A sweet solution to flu?'

6.9

> The recorded discussion focuses on genetic and environmental factors in serious diseases.
>
> Note these key words and phrases:
>
> incidence   early onset
> defect   degenerative
> to subject/be subjected to... carcinogen

6.10
TASK

Complete the following sentences:

1 It is said that you can tell... from examining...
2 The use of DNA samples may help us to...
3 It is clear that heart disease and cancer are not...,
  because the effects of... must also be...
4 Diseases like cystic fibrosis, which mainly affect children
  and young adults,...
5 Degenerative diseases which mainly occur in later life...

6.11 What current issues and fears does this drawing refer to?

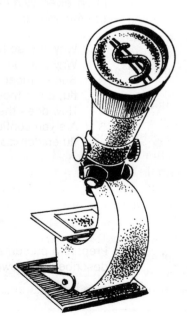

Do modern urban environments present the greatest threat of all to public health?

Not a breath of clean air...

In the latter half of the twentieth century, Mexico City joined a group of Latin American super-conurbations that dwarfed the great cities of Europe and North America. Swollen by internal migration, by 1994 Mexico's capital and its suburbs were home to nineteen million people, nearly a quarter of the nation's population. The area supported some 30,000 factories and over 3.5 million vehicles, many of them old and badly maintained.

In the 1990s the flow of newcomers eased as the government, concerned at the increasing metropolitan sprawl, encouraged migrants to settle elsewhere. Much damage had already been done, however: the capital, still recovering from the 1985 earthquake, showed all too clearly the effects of rapid expansion, lack of investment in infrastructures and unregulated substandard housing. But its greatest problem was atmospheric pollution.

In the Mexico valley, lying at an altitude of 2,230 metres and ringed with wind-calming mountains, the shortage of oxygen – 23 percent less than at sea level – makes combustion processes less efficient and vehicle and factory emissions more harmful. So, in the critical winter months, thermal inversions frequently trapped noxious mixtures of ozone, carbon monoxide and lead above the city, irritating the inhabitants' lungs and making breathing difficult. These pollutants reduced visibility, making the once prized view from the city centre of the region's snow-capped mountains a rarity. And on clear and sunny days photochemical reactions raised ozone levels.

The situation called for drastic government action. Motorists were required to leave their cars at home on one workday every week. Lead-free petrol was introduced, lead levels in regular fuel reduced and twice-weekly emission inspections ordered for all vehicles. Helicopter patrols targeted pollution from industrial sites. These measures lowered the atmospheric lead content by four-fifths and brought carbon monoxide and sulphur dioxide levels under control. But serious problems remained: additives used to enhance octane levels in lead-free petrol actually made ozone levels rise further, while the proportion of potentially lethal air particles remained uncomfortably high. Meanwhile, for Mexicans, the prospect of economic reform and greater prosperity through closer North American trade links made the creation of cleaner industrial and residential environments an increasingly urgent priority.

6.13
TEXT

Which factors are explicitly mentioned in 'Not a breath of clean air...' as contributing to Mexico City's problems? Select the items that apply:

❏ 1 The Mexican government could not persuade migrants to settle in other cities.
❏ 2 Mountains around the Mexico valley reduced wind speeds and made it difficult to get rid of pollutants.
❏ 3 Ozone levels in the atmosphere increased as a result of photochemical reactions and the use of petrol additives.
❏ 4 Many of Mexico City's factories and vehicles were old and inefficient.
❏ 5 The presence of ozone and other pollutants made it difficult for people to breathe.
❏ 6 Mexico City suffered from a lack of oxygen because of frequent thermal inversions.
❏ 7 Mexico City had grown too fast and its development had been badly controlled.

6.14
ANALYSIS

1 Was the action taken by the Mexican government adequate? What further measures might have been taken to address the city's problems?
2 Which was the greater problem – the fact that Mexico City had grown so large, or the fact that its expansion was unregulated?
3 How significant an issue is urban pollution in the major cities that you know well? How are the authorities tackling the problem?

6.15

Summarize this chart in your own words:

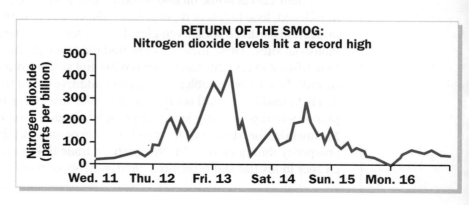

RETURN OF THE SMOG:
Nitrogen dioxide levels hit a record high

**6.16
TASK**

Combine each of the following pairs of sentences, using a gerund:

Example: Thermal inversions trapped noxious mixtures of pollutants/they irritated the inhabitants' lungs.
*Thermal inversions trapped noxious mixtures of pollutants, **irritating** the inhabitants' lungs.*

1   The government responded with drastic measures/they ordered emission inspections for all vehicles.
2   There is a 23 percent loss of oxygen at this altitude/it makes combustion processes less efficient.
3   The authorities introduced lead-free petrol/it reduced lead levels by four-fifths.
4   Mexico could enjoy the prospect of greater prosperity/this made the creation of cleaner environments all the more necessary.
5   The city's population increased to nineteen million/this made it one of the world's largest conurbations.

**6.17
TASK**

Add a prefix (un-, -dis-, over- or anti-) to complete the following sentences:

1   Take a rest! You're suffering from ____work.
2   ____smoking campaigns have been very successful in North America.
3   He felt very ____satisfied with his day's work.
4   I thought the statistics quoted on absence from work through sickness totally ____believable.
5   Many people find commuting so stressful that they are ____inclined to go on working in big cities.

6.18

Find a newspaper report or a magazine article that deals with health issues or medical research. Summarize it and be prepared to answer questions about it.

6.19 Key Vocabulary

additive	to forestall
antibody	genealogical
blatant	genome
blueprint	to impede
carbon monoxide	infrastructure
carcinogen	to infect
catalyst	lethal
chromosome	micro-organism
cleft	molecule
combustion	to mutate/mutation
conurbation	to neutralize
to correlate	noxious
culprit	organism
cystic fibrosis	plume of smoke
defect	predisposition
in defiance of...	protein
degenerative	sequence
diagnostic (test)	site
DNA (deoxyribonucleic acid)	to skyrocket
drastic	spiky
early onset	strain
emissions	to subject/be subjected to...
enzyme	thermal inversion
epidemic	vaccine
	virus/viral

Green issues

When you have finished this chapter you should be able to

■ discuss the impact of climatic change and human
   action on the natural environment, especially in relation
   to food and waste product management

■ express your own views on the effects of human
   intervention on the natural environment

■ understand and use a range of terms employed in
   specialist discussions of these matters

7.1

Warm-up

What effects – good or bad – is global warming likely to have on the world's food supplies?

What evidence is there of climatic change in your country?

Should we wait for scientific proof of these changes before taking action?

7.2

In the recording, an air force pilot and an engineer talk about occasions when the waste of natural resources is virtually unavoidable.

Note these key words and phrases:

fuel consumption	density tap
phenomenal	droplet
training jet	field visit
airborne	pressure blowout/burnout
to dump	to disperse
budgetary	to flare off
clean-up	contaminant

7.3
TASK

Complete the following sentences:

1 Because military jet aircraft have such a high fuel consumption,...
2 If air force units do not use up their fuel allowance...
3 Pressure blowouts in oil pipelines can cause serious problems...
4 If a gas pipeline bursts in the middle of a river,...
5 When a blowout occurs, the gas coming from the wells...

7.4

Imagine that you are a senior manager working for an oil exploration company. Present an argument for more frequent inspection of pipelines.

**7.5
TASK**

To counter global warming, countries must regulate the levels of greenhouse gases CO_2, methane, N_2O, etc.) in the atmosphere. In order to work out who needs to do what, an inventory must be drawn up calculating how much is emitted by sources of greenhouse gases. In reality this is nearly impossible. For each of these sources of greenhouse gases state whether you think we can make a reasonable estimate of their contribution to global warming and, if so, how.

Sources	Calculable?	Method
Cars		
Factories		
Farm slurry		
Rice fields		

**7.6
TASK**

Explain this chart in the light of your understanding of the difficulties of estimating emissions:

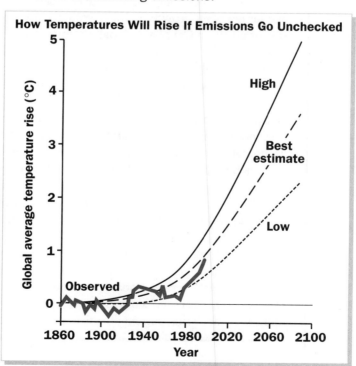

How Temperatures Will Rise If Emissions Go Unchecked

What effect will the increasing emission of greenhouse gases
have on the world's climate?

Global warming and agriculture

Many environmentalists agree that some global warming will take place in the
21st century, however slowly. A 1990 forecast indicated that the average global
temperature would rise by 3° Celsius over the next hundred years. What is far
less certain, though, is the effect that such a temperature rise will have on society.

If global warming does occur, it will be caused by the continuing emission
of greenhouse gases, such as carbon dioxide, methane and nitrogen oxide.
Agriculture, directly or indirectly, is responsible for releasing a high proportion
of these gases. So what can we do to keep our environment stable? Should we
restrict farming? Impossible: we need to improve living standards and go on
producing food for an increasing world population. The efforts of governments
and scientific organizations must therefore be focused on hindering gas
emissions rather than on halting them entirely.

Some scientists suggest that global warming could actually improve agriculture.
With enough water and light, increased carbon dioxide concentrations could
encourage plant growth. In areas with a shorter growing season – Scandinavia,
say, or northern Canada – global warming could help farmers by stretching the
time between the last spring frost and the first frost in the autumn. And as
warmer air holds more water vapour, increased evaporation and precipitation
could spur crop yields in areas where droughts currently limit production.

But the possible negative consequences cannot be ignored. If global warming
does not increase rainfall, farms will suffer more frequent droughts.
Temperature rises in tropical and subtropical areas, where some crops already
approach their limit of heat tolerance, will further reduce harvests. Yields of
crops that require low winter temperatures to encourage flowering would also
fall. The melting of polar ice would swell the oceans, invading low-lying
farmland and increasing coastal salt concentrations.

At present, forecasts of the effects of global warming are still unreliable. But
many tend to be pessimistic: one recent analysis of the impact of climatic change,
suggesting that average global food production will fall by five per cent by 2060,
indicates that the reduction will be more serious in the developing economies,
apparently defeating current efforts to provide for their growing populations.

7.8
TASK

In which paragraphs of 'Global warming and agriculture' do you find the following information? How is it expressed in the text?

1   It is still not known exactly how much society will be affected by a global rise in temperature.
2   A rise in the level of the sea might cause flooding of farmland close to sea-level.
3   More water vapour is present in warmer air.
4   The poorer countries may have far less food in the future.
5   In some regions, it is already almost too hot to grow some crops.

7.9
ANALYSIS

1   In your view, can the growing food needs of increasing human populations be reconciled with the need to reduce plant emissions?
2   What beneficial effects will global warming have, according to the text? Do you feel that these benefits can be satisfactorily managed?
3   Do you know of any specific geographic areas where the effects of global warming – such as a rise in ocean levels – would be particularly pronounced? How aware are the inhabitants of these effects, in your view?
4   If you were a farmer in northern Canada, what would be your feelings about global warming?

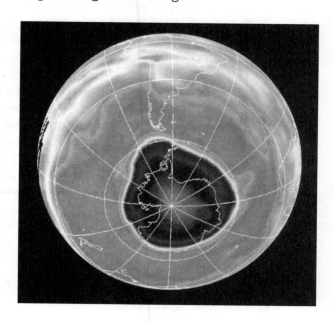

7.10
TEXT

After nearly two decades of fisheries management, overfishing in the waters of developed countries is worse than ever. Is conservation a lost cause, and are people too greedy to be effective managers of the world's fish resources?

Net losses

The catch in developed countries has fallen back to the levels of the early 1970s. Catches of Atlantic cod off the northwest American coast peaked at 800,000 tonnes in 1968 and collapsed in the 1970s. In 1992 managers recommended a catch of less than 50,000 tonnes; Canada closed the fishery altogether. In the North Sea, the spawning cod stock fell to 66,000 tonnes in 1990, barely a third of the Food and Agriculture Organization's safe minimum.

In some waters, management has merely brought the foolishness of overfishing into the open. In 1975 the Alaskan fleet enjoyed a season for Pacific halibut lasting 120 days. The fleet can now take the year's entire catch in one or two 24-hour 'derbys'. If fishing went on longer, there would be too few halibut to spawn future catches. (The Alaskan herring-roe fishery is open for a mere 40 minutes a year.) Boats queue to sell their catch to processors, who gut and freeze the year's supply as quickly as they can.

Having failed in Europe and America, fisheries management threatens to fail in developing countries, too. A few, such as Namibia, are introducing sensible management early on, even before the fleet is overcapitalised. More, however, are repeating the mistakes made in the rich countries by building up fleets without regard to the size of their fishing stocks, sometimes with subsidies from development agencies.

Fishermen are not happy with overfishing but see no alternative. Few have any faith in the government managers who have curbed their independence but have not delivered the plenty that was promised. They (correctly) see that fisheries science is inexact, but (wrongly) deduce that the scientists' estimates of a safe catch are always too low. Even if they trusted the fisheries managers, many fishermen would worry more about paying the mortgages on their boats.

The Economist

7.11
TASK

Rewrite the sentences using the words in capitals:

Example: Fisheries management has failed in Europe and
America. It threatens to fail in developing
countries, too. HAVING
Having failed *in Europe and America, fisheries
management threatens to fail in developing
countries, too.*

1   Many developing countries are repeating the rich
countries' mistakes. They have increased the size of
their fishing fleets. IN ...ING
2   Managers have curbed the fishermen's independence.
They have not delivered the plenty they promised.
WITHOUT ...ING
3   Cod catches off the northwest US coast peaked in the
1960s. They collapsed in the 1970s. HAVING
4   The aircraft had to turn back because of the weather. It
then dumped its fuel. AFTER ...ING
5   The engineers closed the valves to the gas pipeline. All
they could do was to burn the gas off. AFTER ...ING

7.12
TASK

*Complete the following sentences with the correct form of one of
the words in the pairs:*

blame/cause:
1   The _____ of the oil blowout was never discovered.
2   Insurance investigators tried to discover who was to _____.
3   Investigators laid the _____ on the pilot of the aircraft
that dumped the chemicals.
4   The accident at the car showroom _____ the military to
open an investigation.
result/effect:
5   The _____ of overfishing is a severe shortage of fish.
6   The increase in the size of fishing fleets has had an
alarming _____ on fish stocks.
7   As a _____ of extra subsidies, more fishing vessels
were built.
limit/extent:
8   Canada closed the cod fishery when managers
recommended a _____ of less than 50,000 tonnes.
9   The full _____ of the storm damage could be seen the
next morning.
10   The _____ of the damage to fish stocks caused by the
blowout could be clearly seen.

**7.13
TASK**

Explain the following charts, relating to world fishing levels:

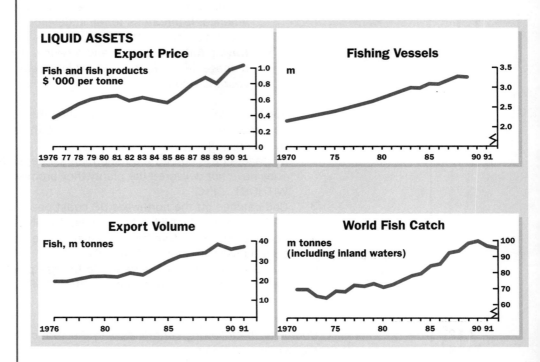

7.14

'The problem with human interference with the environment is not so much the changes that people make as the inadequate planning and risk assessment that precede the changes.' How far do you agree with this statement?

**7.15
ROLE PLAY**

A government representative (Role **A** – page 122) and a fisherman (Role **B** – page 124) discuss a solution to overfishing.

7.16

In the recording a senior business executive discusses some environment-friendly measures and projects.

Note these key words and phrases:

to harness
energy efficiency,
  energy-efficient
product recycling
chiller
heat reclaim
best practice
air conditioner

'cradle to grave'
obsolete
to step up
compliance
in proportion to...
to have an uncanny knack of...
to tarnish a reputation

**7.17
TASK**

Complete the following sentences:

1 IBM UK's policy on energy conservation includes...
2 The company is saving £27,000 a year by installing...
3 From an audit, IBM UK found that...
4 Some 80 per cent of IBM UK's obsolete computing equipment...
5 The EU is anxious to ensure that member countries...
6 In the USA, fines imposed on polluters...
7 A company's reputation can easily be tarnished...

7.18

'Financial penalties do not protect the environment. By the time a corporation is caught violating a regulation the damage to the environment has already been done.' Discuss.

7.19

You are a senior manager in a large manufacturing company. Present an outline of an environment-friendly policy to your fellow-managers, emphasizing the bottom-line benefits to the organization.

7.20 | # Key Vocabulary

airborne	field visit
air conditioner	fisheries
best practice	to flare off
bottom-line benefit	to harness
budgetary	heat reclaim
catch	methane
chiller	mortgage
clean-up	obsolete
company image	to overfish
compliance	phenomenal
contaminant	precipitation
'cradle to grave'	pressure blowout/burnout
crop yield	in proportion to...
density tap	to recycle
'derby'	to spawn
to disperse	to step up
droplet	to tarnish a reputation
to dump	training jet
energy efficiency	to have an uncanny knack of..
energy-efficient	vapour (Br)/vapor (Am)
evaporation	

Predicting the future

When you have finished this chapter you should be able to

■ distinguish between scientific and non-scientific predictions

■ appreciate the value of non-scientific means of prediction

■ assess the quality of claims to knowing the future

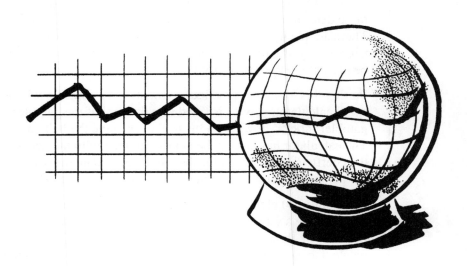

8.1

Warm-up

What is the difference between these weather forecasts?
What makes one of them scientific?

- "The low pressure weather system will bring cooler temperatures."

- "Red sky at night, sailor's delight." (An old saying forecasting good weather the next day)

8.2
TEXT

Is playing roulette a suitable area for scientific experiments?

Freedom and friction

Can you predict the result of a spin of a roulette wheel? Conventional wisdom holds that certain gambling ventures can be approached scientifically while others cannot. Poker, horse racing and financial speculation can combine the scientific – mathematics, probability, observation – with the unscientific – intuition, psychology, etc. Roulette, on the other hand, is one area that no serious gambler would stray into unless he knew that the wheel was fixed. If you were to play roulette according to the rules of probability you would have to spend so long at the table making observations you would hardly ever get round to placing a bet.

But does it have to be this way? After all, where the ball ultimately comes to rest is determined by three physical phenomena: the relative speeds of the ball and the wheel, friction, and where the ball enters the wheel. In mathematics these determining factors are known as the 'degrees of freedom' in the system. There are plenty of other systems with three degrees of freedom, such as the flight of a golf ball, which can be calculated with great accuracy, so it should be possible in the case of roulette.

Putting this logic into practice, scientists have come up with an answer. A small calculating device is fitted into the heel of the gambler's shoe. The gambler 'clicks' down with his heel every time the ball passes a certain point. The calculator has already been programmed with the necessary formulae and the coefficient of friction for the wheel. Instantaneously a read-out wired up to the gambler's hand gives a number and the bet is placed.

One additional element however throws a spanner in the works. Most roulette wheels have a series of metal 'studs' placed just above the numbers at intervals of about every fourth space on the wheel. This adds a further (and incalculable) degree of freedom to the system, the result being that the machine can only be sure of predicting within four spaces of the correct answer.

8.3
TASK

For each item listed below find a term in the text which has the same meaning:

1   engineered to give an unfair advantage
2   general informed opinion
3   an information display panel
4   to block or impede something
5   a number used for mathematical calculations
6   knowledge which has no factual basis
7   immediately

8.4
TASK

Which of the following are suggested by the text 'Freedom and friction'? Select the items that apply:

❏   1   There's lots of money to be made from roulette.
❏   2   The flight of a golf ball can be accurately predicted.
❏   3   Psychology and intuition are thought of as scientific.
❏   4   Given time the laws of probability could be used on roulette.
❏   5   All systems with three degrees of freedom are predictable.
❏   6   Many professional gamblers employ a combination of science and non-science.

8.5
TASK

Complete the following sentences with the words in the box below:

1   I have _____ been to a casino. I don't believe in throwing my money away.
2   They have _____ sold a thousand devices.
3   Has that horse _____ won a race?
4   You would have to watch the wheel _____ a long time to see a pattern.
5   Gamblers have not _____ found a way to win at roulette.
6   Such a machine has been sought _____ the roulette wheel was invented.

for	yet	already
never	ever	since

8.6
TASK

What are the degrees of freedom in the following systems? Which one is the most difficult to predict?

- winning a hand in a game of poker

- picking the winner in a horse race

- forecasting tomorrow's weather

8.7

In the recording, a consultant explains a fourfold approach to anticipating and identifying trends in society. How did this activity develop?

Note these key words and phrases:

a brief	to split
to anticipate	cocooning
straightforward	down-ag(e)ing
field	brainstorming
notoriety	

8.8
TASK

Complete the following sentences:

1   The design consultancy needed a business process which...
2   Faith Popcorn's Brain Reserve is concerned with...
3   The 'cocooning' trend in the USA has arisen because...
4   By putting all the trends in a society together, experts hope...
5   Brainstorming is useful in business planning...

8.9

Identify the 4 elements to the system outlined in the recording, then match each one with the corresponding description on the right:

1 _____   asking specialists

2 _____   geographical analysis

3 _____   discussing random ideas

4 _____   asking people in the street

8.10

"Cocooning" and "down-aging" are two American consumer trends. What others have you noticed in your country? Could they have been predicted using the system you have been hearing about?

8.11

In the recording, two consultants discuss the trends towards customization and standardization in consumer goods industries.

Note these key words and phrases:

customization   handlebar grip
standardization   mass-produced
emphasis on   antithesis
to specify   to slim (slimline)

**8.12
TASK**

Complete the following sentences:

1　Japanese manufacturers abandoned standardized products...
2　They are now concerned with combining mass production...
3　Toyota reduced the number of customer options on the Lexus...
4　In order to simplify production, ...
5　It may in the future be simpler for manufacturers to...

**8.13
TASK**

A　*Rewrite the following sentences, using 'What...doing/does':*

Example:　Toyota are cutting down choice and simplifying production.
What Toyota **are doing is** cutting down choice and simplifying production.

1　I think he is working too hard.
2　New approaches to manufacturing are increasing customer choice.
3　Rover are offering a quarter million different models.
4　A small calculator produces a read-out.
5　Brainstorming helps business planners formulate ideas.

B　*Complete the following sentences, using 'What...doing...' and the correct form of the verb in capitals:*

1　What professional gamblers _____.　FIND
2　What customization _____.　PROVIDE
3　What standardization _____.　LIMIT

8.14

In the second recording, two seemingly opposite trends have emerged. Either it is pointless trying to predict consumer behaviour, or we need complex systems like the one described in the first recording to make the correct prediction.　Which conclusion do you agree with?

The idea that financial markets can be predicted is no longer thought eccentric. How can mathematical theories help us to understand their behaviour?

Are financial trends predictable?

Can the behaviour of the financial markets be predicted? They involve all the elements which would make a scientist run a mile: human reactions, too many variables and no evidence that any one system of picking winners is any better than just sitting on a portfolio of investments. Yet in spite of these objections, computerized trading systems are the major players in several markets.

The explosion in automated trading has been a result of three developments: the discovery of predictability in human reactions to news, mathematical techniques, and computers powerful enough to assimilate all the information which is needed.

It has long been known that fluctuations in the financial markets are not random. Some observers compare them to the weather: just as an anticyclone that has been around for days is likely to persist, so an upward or downward market trend is likely to be reinforced – possibly because people like to follow fashions. In this way human reactions become predictable, removing one variable element from the process.

The mathematical development chiefly concerns the field known as fractal theory. This holds that apparently random processes can reveal patterns if you study them correctly. It yields interesting results, such as the fact that the average differences between foreign exchange price movements over one day and two days are substantially the same as those over one year and two years.

This has caused friction between economists and mathematicians. Economists cite a golden law of economics that you must first look at how people behave and then predict their effects. What the mathematicians are doing is starting from the data and applying their theories without caring why their theories work.

The computer program will, however, need regular updating. Whereas the weather now has the same causes acting upon it as a century ago (humidity, sea-surface temperature and so on), the causes of trends in the financial markets change regularly. Oil prices may be the prime mover at one time, dollar interest rates at another. The mathematicians will always need to work in conjunction with economists to keep up with these developments.

8.16
TASK

Rewrite the following sentences using the words in capitals:

Example: Mathematicians will need to work with economists
           to keep up with developments. IN ORDER
           ***In order** to keep up with developments,
           mathematicians will need to work with economists.*

1   Can the behaviour of the financial markets be predicted?
    POSSIBLE
2   It has long been known that fluctuations in the financial
    markets are not random. LONG TIME/UNPREDICTABLE
3   The explosion in automated trading has been a result of
    three developments. THREE/RESULTED
4   The computer program will, however, need regular
    updating. NEED TO BE/BASIS

8.17
TASK

*Which one verb can you use before all the nouns or noun
phrases in the box?*

a fight	a winner
his pocket	holes in his argument
her brains	two sides

Now complete the sentences with full phrases from the box:

1   The young boys _____ of eleven players before they
    started the game.
2   He felt the man _____ as he went into the station,
    and saw him run off with his wallet.
3   He phoned up his friend, who was a lawyer, to _____
    about his legal rights.
4   The two young men _____ with the elderly man, not
    realizing he was an ex-boxing champion.
5   She tried to _____, but he had thought everything
    through very carefully.
6   His way of trying to _____ was to close his eyes and
    stick a pin in the list of horses in the race.

**8.18
TASK**

Complete the right-hand column with the correct nouns:

Example: mathematics   *mathematician*

1 economics   _____
2 science   _____
3 chemistry   _____
4 meteorology   _____
5 astronomy   _____
6 languages   _____

8.19

What would the effect be if all investors eventually used automatic trading systems? How would it change the shapes of these graphs? Prepare a brief presentation.

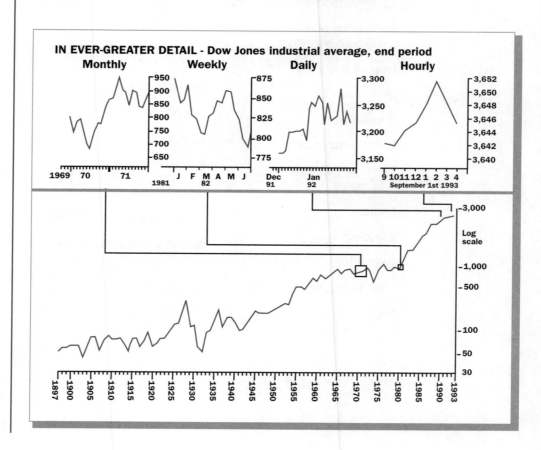

8.20 Key Vocabulary

anti-cyclone	identical
to anticipate	in conjunction with...
antithesis	incalculable
to assimilate	intuition
brainstorming	mass-produced
brief	techniques
cocooning	notoriety
coefficient	phenomenon
conventional wisdom	portfolio
customization	predictability
down-aging *(Am)/* down-ageing *(Br)*	read-out
emphasis on	to reinforce
field	to slim (slimline)
fluctuation	to specify
foreign exchange	to split
formulae *(pl)*, *also* formulas	standardization
	straightforward
friction	substantially
gambling	to throw a spanner in the works
golden law	
handlebar grip	to update
humidity	variable

Environmental awareness

When you have completed this chapter you should be able to

- discuss how technology can be used to address environmental problems and how people can be involved in applying it

- express your own views on the scientific and technological aspects of ecological issues

- understand and use a range of related terms

9.1

Warm-up

Is noise pollution a serious problem in the country as well as in the city?

Which should be a greater environmental priority: helping small communities achieve visible goals, or tackling global problems?

Should companies and households pay to have their rubbish removed?

9.2

Are low-flying aircraft a threat to rural communities? In the recording a specialist explains some aspects of noise pollution.

Note these key words and phrases:

the defence industry	chicken coop
420 knots	natural cycle
to impact	wildlife sanctuary
livelihood	low-level flying

9.3
TASK

Complete the following sentences:

1 As aircraft technology has improved,...
2 When a low-flying aircraft passes, chickens...
3 Aircraft noise can also impact severely on...
4 A jet aircraft can be brought down...
5 As a result of political agitation,...

9.4

Is it justifiable to export problems such as noise pollution to remote areas instead of banning it completely?

Many people in the West find it astonishing that basic benefits can be brought to disadvantaged communities in Africa and elsewhere at so low a cost. How can this be achieved?

Pipe dreams can come true...

Imagine having to walk twelve miles to the nearest water. Then imagine sitting beside a hollow for hours, collecting the merest trickles of water – which will have to last the family three days – before carrying it back another twelve miles; in all, a round trip of between six and eight hours. That's what the women of Hitosa, Ethiopia, have to do every day – and they still can't get enough water for their families' needs.

Bringing adequate supplies of safe water to Hitosa is a job which will take about three years to complete. The British-based charity WaterAid will be working with local organizations and the community itself. We will provide part of the money and most of the back-breaking labour required.

Tragically, a high child mortality rate and water-related illnesses, such as dysentery and diarrhea, are common among the people of Hitosa. But now, building on the success of a similar scheme, WaterAid is helping to lay fifty miles of pipe to bring safe water to the 56,000 people who need it – the largest and most ambitious project the charity has ever supported.

However, the work at Hitosa isn't just about saving the villagers the long walk. It includes health education and training the community in maintenance skills. The result will be a lasting water supply, a healthier community and fewer deaths among the children.

For the people of Ethiopia and elsewhere in the Third World, donations to Western charities such as WaterAid can mean a healthier future. For example, £25 will buy the taps needed for a water point serving 800 people in the Hitosa gravity scheme. £50 currently buys enough guttering to provide safe water for three families in a rainwater harvesting project in India. £100 will match the local contributions required to hire a skilled mason to protect four springs serving 800 people in Uganda. And administrative costs can be kept low. In 1992/93, 90% of our expenditure directly supported projects overseas; only 10% was spent on administration.

Charity Commission Reg. no. 288701

9.6
TASK

In which paragraphs of 'Pipe dreams can come true' do you find the following information? How is it expressed in the text?

1   The names of two illnesses caused by poor water
2   The fact that Ethiopia is a less-developed country
3   Where WaterAid has its headquarters
4   That the Hitosa project involves education as well as construction

9.7
TASK

Rewrite the following sentences, using the correct form of the words in capitals.

Example: It will take about three years to finish bringing adequate supplies of safe water to Hitosa.
JOB/COMPLETE
*Bringing adequate supplies of safe water to Hitosa is a **job which** will take about three years **to complete**.*

1   How did they get the money needed for the project?
WAS/OBTAIN
2   In all, it was a round trip of eight hours. EACH WAY
3   The result will be a lasting water supply, a healthier community, and fewer deaths among the children.
PERMANENT/BETTER HEALTH/MORTALITY
4   A £100 donation will match the local contributions required to hire a skilled mason. £200/HALF/HALF
5   This is the largest and most ambitious project the charity has ever supported. NEVER BEFORE/SO

9.8

1   Charities helping the developing world are sometimes criticized for spending too much on liaison and public relations. How would you ensure that the administrative costs of schemes such as WaterAid are kept low?
2   What implications do you think the health education and community training programs have for the Hitosa villagers and similar communities?

**9.9
ROLE PLAY**

Two people who work for a charity discuss the use of funds. One (Role **A** – page 123) wants to spend more on advertising and raising awareness, while the other (Role **B** – page 125) wants to use money for projects.

9.10

In the recording the discussion of measures to combat aircraft noise pollution is continued.

Note these key words and phrases:

civil aircraft	white noise
takeoff	aeronautics
descent	rotor
steep	air frame
radius	vibration
a baffle	fatigue life
(still) air molecules	turbulence
wiggly	

9.11
TASK

Complete the following sentences:

1 Takeoffs and descents of civil aircraft are now...
2 The steeper your climb away from the ground,...
3 Jet engines are noisy because molecules...
4 Flying in helicopters can be uncomfortable because...
5 Westland have tried to combat airframe vibrations by...
6 Airframe fatigue life is determined by...

9.12
TASK

Which of the following is suggested in the recording? Select the items that apply:

❑ 1 White noise causes more vibrations in aircraft but reduces noise.
❑ 2 White noise causes more noise in aircraft but reduces vibrations.
❑ 3 Steeper takeoffs are noisier because they require more power.
❑ 4 Baffles make air move more smoothly.
❑ 5 Worn-out aircraft are noisier than new ones.
❑ 6 Noise is created by friction between air molecules.

Can recycling agencies become dangerous monopolies?

The green dot: Germany's recycling strategy runs into problems

In Germany, 80 percent of consumer product packaging carries a green dot, indicating that the material has to be consigned to a special yellow recycling bin instead of to the conventional black rubbish container. The system is operated by Duales System Deutschland (DSD), a nationwide waste collection agency and a symbol of an intended national commitment to environmental protection.

However, the scheme has its critics. In the early 1990s the Federal Cartel Office opened an investigation into the activities of DSD, concerned that the fast-growing scheme was creating a monopoly. At the same time, large numbers of environmentalists began to express anxiety about the system, seeing it as a fig-leaf used by industrialists to avoid investment in ecological policies.

DSD was set up when the German Federal Parliament passed a law in 1990 requiring manufacturers to recover and reuse packaging waste. The law stipulates that by 1 July 1995 manufacturers must ensure that 80 percent of all packaging is collected and that 80 percent of this amount is recycled – although during the first phase, from 1 January 1993, lower proportions have been accepted: 60 percent of glass, 40 percent of tinplate, 30 percent of aluminium, paper, cardboard and plastic.

Legislation also obliges the German states or Länder to nominate a central waste collection and recycling agency. Most states have chosen DSD, which intends to expand its activity from 95 percent of urban areas into the small business sector. This venture has led the Berlin-based national cartel office to seek to fix operating limits for the agency. DSD sees the investigators' move as unjustified. 'The law obliges us to act as a nationwide monopoly,' says a spokeswoman, 'and having to organize industrial waste collection just imposes an extra burden on us. Besides, we are a non-profit organization.'

That is substantially true. DSD's expenses are covered by the extra two pfennigs that each consumer pays at the supermarket for green-dot packaging. The loudest complaints against the agency have been voiced not by consumers but by small recycling enterprises, which depend on DSD to collect and supply the waste they process; they claim that DSD's expansion will stifle competitive opportunity in the recycling industry.

**9.14
TASK**

Which factors are explicitly identified in 'The green dot' as characteristic of or applying to DSD? Select the items that apply:

- ❏ 1   DSD is a nationwide expression of German commitment to environmental protection.
- ❏ 2   DSD offers an easy way for industries to show token interest in environmental policies.
- ❏ 3   DSD implements regulations designed to ensure that most packaging is collected and recycled.
- ❏ 4   German states are required to use DSD as a waste collection agency.
- ❏ 5   DSD plans to extend its operations from the manufacturing sector to the small business sector.
- ❏ 6   Smaller recycling enterprises view DSD's plans as likely to limit their own business opportunities.
- ❏ 7   National cartel office investigators are seeking to limit DSD's operations.

9.15

'Recycling is too time-consuming and too expensive to be regarded as a serious activity by industrialists.' How far do you agree with this statement?

**9.16
ROLE PLAY**

A group of townspeople are trying to put together a local recycling policy. An industrial manager (Role **A** – page 123) opposes plans put forward by a pressure group (Role **B** – page 125) on the grounds that they will cost too much to implement.

9.17
TASK

Rewrite the sentences so as to explain the meanings of the words in boldface type:

Example: Environmentalists saw the system as **a fig-leaf** used by industrialists **to avoid investment** in ecological policies.
*Environmentalists saw the system as **a way** for industrialists **to hide their unwillingness to invest** in ecological policies.*

1   Many feel that by sponsoring development projects the West is **holding out an olive branch** to the Third World.
2   It was thought to be one of the most enterprising charities in the country, but overspending proved to be its **Achilles' heel**.
3   Zimbabwe is often considered to be **the breadbasket** of southern Africa.
4   Rich Western companies that refuse to donate to developing-world charities could be said to **show a dog-in-the-manger attitude**.
5   If you're running a charity, you must ensure that as much money as possible reaches the people you want to help – so you must **tighten the purse-strings**.
6   Populations accustomed to going short of food may be resentful of societies that **live high off the hog**.

9.18

Find a newspaper report or an article in a magazine that addresses the issue of technological aid to developing countries or the problem of waste disposal in more advanced economies. Summarize it and be ready to answer questions on it.

9.19 | Key Vocabulary

aeronautics	low-level flying
air frame	monopoly
(still) air molecules	mortality rate
aluminium*(Br)/* aluminum*(Am)*	natural cycle
back-breaking	packaging
a baffle	radius
cartel	recycling
chicken coop	rotor
civil aircraft	small business sector
commitment	steep
the defence industry	takeoff
descent	tap
diarrhea	tin plate
donation	trickle
dysentery	turbulence
fatigue life	vibration
guttering	white noise
to impact	wiggly
420 knots	wildlife sanctuary
livelihood	

10

Getting about and keeping in touch

When you have completed this chapter you should be able to

■ discuss urban transport problems and ways in which electronic communications can help people on the move

■ express your own views on the problems of urban transport and communications

■ understand and use a range of related terms

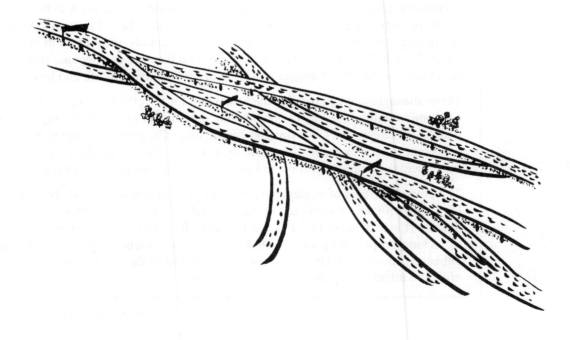

Warm-up

Cities offer no economic advantages unless the people who work in them can move about them easily. Can today's societies still afford to use private cars in large urban areas?

Can today's conurbations still provide efficient systems for moving people, products, money and information?

Transport and urban survival

The growth of urban productivity depends on swift and cheap connections between homes and workplaces, between ports or airports and factories. The heart of the modern metropolis is also the movement of information and finance. In the case of finance, the past twenty years have seen extraordinary growth, transforming central business districts. But participation depends on increasingly sophisticated telecommunication systems connecting cities as well as on a facilitating political and administrative framework. In many developing countries, private capital is being brought to bear to develop this capacity.

Compared to the investment lavished on international movement, city transport is a Cinderella – even though the economic advantages of the city and the productivity of the city worker depend on swift and cheap local movement.

The situation is getting painfully worse in most cities as a generation of investment reaches exhaustion, without being renewed, while the numbers requiring to travel grow spectacularly. There are said to be 1.7 million vehicles (including two-wheelers) added to India's stock annually, most of them in cities. Vehicle domination of roads collides with the masses of people still dependent on muscle or animal power, with severe threats to life and limb.

Urban management can provide the leadership for the efforts to secure the economic future of the city by maintaining an efficient system to manage flows: people, goods, services, information and finance. The paradox of development is present in each element – increasingly swift and cheap long-distance movement for a minority, slow and extravagant city movement for the majority.

The present failures of management trap the poor in isolated islands between high-speed routes, crisscrossed by aircraft and rail and road viaducts. Transport, which should be a means to escape from poverty, becomes a means of locking people into ghettoes. On all counts – the amelioration of poverty, the enhancement of productivity and the improvement of the environment – effective urban management is a key to progress.

Nigel Harris in The Urban Age

**10.3
TASK**

Make one sentence from the three provided:

Example: The situation is getting painfully worse in most
cities. We are exhausting a generation of
investment. We are not renewing it.
*The situation is getting painfully worse in most
cities as a generation of investment reaches
exhaustion, without being renewed.*

1   City management is becoming more and more ineffective.
We are trapping the poor in isolated ghettos. They cannot
easily escape.
2   The economic advantages of the city are increasingly
questioned. City workers are becoming less productive.
They are not offered cheaper and swifter transport.
3   Urban management is becoming a paradox. It enables a
minority of people to enjoy swift travel. It does not make
similar advantages available to most city-dwellers.

**10.4
TASK**

Solutions to the problems of urban congestion:

Low-Tech

- Toll roads
- "No Stopping" routes
  through city centres
- Building roads

High-Tech

- Home-based offices
- Electric cars
- In-car radar warning
  drivers of congested routes

How effective have the solutions on the left been in cities you
know?
Will the solutions on the right be any more successful?

How can a city such as Bangkok deal with escalating problems of traffic congestion, with 500 new vehicles added to its streets every day?

Bangkok's urban transport crisis

The horrendous traffic in the Bangkok Metropolitan Region is widely known: anyone who has travelled to Thailand has his or her own favorite horror story of being stuck in gridlock for hours. Traffic conditions in Bangkok are generally recognized as being among the worst in the world.

Unplanned and uncoordinated development in this metropolis of nine million (fourteen percent of the country's population) is characterized by massive urban sprawl radiating up to 50 kilometers in all directions. Traffic congestion and air pollution from vehicles are causing substantial economic losses and serious health effects, which mean lost work days and lower productivity.

Sprawling development along major road corridors and inefficient patterns of urbanization have 'frozen' substantial areas of land from development since access to the surrounding road networks is lacking. As land prices escalate, the government has had more difficulty acquiring land for local distributor roads and major highways. High land values have also contributed to high-rise, high-density developments that put additional pressures on existing local infrastructure, especially roads.

In recent years, traffic volume on the main roads has been growing at between 15 and 20 percent per year, representing a doubling in volume every five to six years. More than 500 new vehicles are added to the streets of Bangkok daily, and average travel speeds of less than ten kilometers per hour drop to a mere five or six kilometers per hour in peak traffic periods. This should not be surprising, since roads only occupy eleven percent of Bangkok's total land area, compared with 20-25 percent in such cities as London, Paris and New York.

While the city's roads are clogged with vehicles, its river, canals and railway carry relatively few passengers. Although mass rail transit systems have been proposed for many years, as yet no system has been implemented. The road system consists of a limited number of major arterials, a network of wide main roads, and many small local access roads or *soi*. Many of the main roads, particularly in the inner areas, are operated one-way, with six or more lanes of traffic. This makes them exceedingly difficult for pedestrians to cross. Outside the Middle Ring Road surrounding the inner city, the network is sparsely developed. Several proposed major roads and expressways are in various stages of negotiation, and many smaller roads are under construction.

Rod Stickland in The Urban Age

10.6
TASK

Complete the following sentences:

1 In Bangkok, lost work days and lower productivity…
2 The growing traffic volume on Bangkok's roads has resulted…
3 Non-road traffic in Bangkok seems to… and has not been integrated…
4 Western cities have an advantage over Bangkok in that…
5 The problems affecting pedestrians in such cities are…

10.7
TASK

In which paragraphs of 'Bangkok's urban transport crisis' are the following subjects mentioned? How are the ideas expressed in the text?

1   Bangkok's annual percentage increase in traffic
2   Bangkok's poor traffic conditions compared to the rest of the world
3   The Thai name for small roads that allow local access
4   The fact that there are large areas of land undeveloped because they are difficult to reach
5   Bangkok's population compared with Thailand's as a whole

10.8

In cities such as Bangkok, can efficient traffic management only be achieved by adopting the most drastic measures and by exploiting non-road traffic systems?

10.9

The recorded discussion considers how advances in electronic communications have allowed more people to work away from city centres.

Note these key words and phrases:

office environment	to start from scratch
downtown	town planning
core	social interaction
to commute	a car-obsessed culture

10.10
TASK

Complete the following sentences:

1   Home computers, fax and improved telephone links have...
2   Some research seems to indicate that people...
3   If planners were to start all over from scratch...
4   It seems that people enjoy social interaction... but don't...
5   If their work moves out of the downtown core, drivers...

How will the use of mobile phones make it easier to link workers together in their homes or in satellite businesses?

A world in which you need never lose touch

There is more to digital phones than clearer speech and greater coverage. The extra airspace brought by digital broadcasting means operators can add features that were impossible on more restricted analogue systems, such as voice mail.

If someone calls your number while it is in use, switched off or outside the coverage area, a 'message waiting' indicator warns you next time you use the phone. Call waiting and call barring are also included, and for an extra fee the cost-conscious can set a monthly limit on call charges. But technological developments for digital phone users are on the way which will transform the simple portable phone into an all-in-one communications organizer.

The 'short message service' allows the mobile phone to be used as an intelligent paging system. If your telephone is on, it will automatically pick up a short, pager-style text message from an information service or another compatible phone – 'Ring office urgently,' 'Share index reaches new high' – all on its own.

Call ID will show you the number of an incoming caller before you pick up the call. Conference calling will allow as many as six people to talk together on the same line. In addition, since the mobile telephone now speaks the same language as a personal computer, it will become a natural way to communicate with the office through a notebook PC. Until the arrival of digital links, notebook computers have had some serious problems in handling analogue portable lines.

Soon, all those communications tools you associate with the office – fax, data transfer, electronic mail – will shrink down into the A4 footprint of a portable PC. They may even get smaller. Computer hardware companies are already working on personal electronic 'assistants', hand-held machines such as the Apple Newton that will eventually incorporate telephone, fax, paging, diary and messaging facilities in a box little bigger than today's mobile handsets.

Being digital promises a world in which you need never lose touch, by telephone, fax, electronic mail – even information services that beam market prices, world news or sports results to your personal, portable communications centre.

Harry Davidson, The Observer

10.12
TASK

Which aspects of electronic communications devices are explicitly identified in 'A world in which you need never lose touch' as significant for effective business information? Select the items that apply:

- ❏ 1 The availability of paging facilities
- ❏ 2 A 'call ID' facility for screening incoming calls
- ❏ 3 Audio conferencing facilities sharing the same line
- ❏ 4 In-car phone facilities
- ❏ 5 Desktop computer e-mail
- ❏ 6 Hand-held fax and messaging facilities
- ❏ 7 Combined video and computer display screens

10.13
TASK

Rewrite the following sentences, using the words in capitals:

Example: Conference calling will allow as many as six people to talk together on the same line. LET/UP TO
*Conference calling will **let up to** six people talk together on the same line.*

1 Underground railway systems have been under construction for some years in many cities but are still far from operational. LONG WAY/BEING
2 The transport challenge is one of the most serious problems faced by cities in the developing world. HAVE TO/CONTEND WITH
3 The number of privately owned cars has increased sharply. SHOW/RISE
4 Digital communications promise a world in which you need never lose touch. OFFER/POSSIBILITY

10.14

Three strategies have been suggested to tackle urban congestion:

- ■ improving public transport, traffic control systems
- ■ working from the home with better communications
- ■ moving business districts to less densely populated areas

What factors limit the potential of each of these strategies?

10.15 TASK

Complete the following sentences with compound adjectives from the box below.

Example: Commuting to a _____ office is rarely a pleasant experience.
*Commuting to a **city-centre** office is rarely a pleasant experience.*

1 There are _____ rumours that a new traffic scheme is to be introduced.
2 The more _____ of our administrators are always looking for ways to reduce expenditure.
3 The exact size of next year's transport budget seems to be a _____ secret.
4 The authorities are making _____ attempts to solve the traffic problem.
5 To isolate the poorer sections of the city was an _____ course of action.
6 The authorities have been altogether too _____ in letting these problems develop.
7 Narrow roads should not be used by _____ vehicles.

easy-going	ill-advised
cost-conscious	well-founded
half-hearted	**city-centre**
high-speed	well-kept

10.16

Find an advertisement for an item of telecommunications equipment, such as a fax machine or a mobile phone. Prepare a presentation in which you summarize its features and discuss its implications for today's society.

10.17 | # Key Vocabulary

amelioration	gridlock
to bring to bear	hand-held
call-waiting	infrastructure
call-barring	to lavish... on...
a car-obsessed culture	metropolis
to commute	muscle power
compatible	office environment
core	paging system
corridor	peak periods
cost-conscious	pedestrian
coverage/coverage area	portable PC (personal computer)
to crisscross	productivity
digital phone	social interaction
downtown	spectacular
enhancement	to start from scratch
exhaustion	telecommunications
extravagant	town planning
to facilitate	urban sprawl
footprint (of computer, etc.)	traffic flow
framework	viaduct
ghetto	workplace

11

Communications and work

When you have finished this chapter you should be able to

■ discuss probable future work patterns and organization

■ express your own views on the opportunities and problems presented by electronic communications in and away from the workplace

■ understand and use a range of related terms

11.1

Warm-up

What are the implications of current innovations in telecommunications for those who are now working at office desks? Will global networks make them more productive?

Will such developments mean that organizations will be less tied to time and place and less reliant on a permanent workforce?

11.2

The recorded discussion considers the need for businesses to make the most of modern technologies and looks at the advantages that such innovations may bring.

Note these key words and phrases from the discussion:

look-alike products	'just in time' business
explosion	to fall behind
cellular phone	graphics
overnight delivery	to network
cable news	computer architecture
to ship	rugged
threshold	resolution

11.3
TASK

Complete the following sentences:

1   The computer has certainly changed the way people work, but...
2   If we are to conduct business faster, we...
3   'Just in time' business communication offers...
4   It is quite possible that the PC has now...
5   While microprocessor performance has increased rapidly,...

11.4
TASK

Which of the following are seen as deficiencies of PCs? Select the items that apply:

- ❑ 1   not enough memory
- ❑ 2   not powerful enough for complex graphics
- ❑ 3   good for individuals but not for businesses
- ❑ 4   good for businesses but not for individuals
- ❑ 5   difficult to connect to other PCs
- ❑ 6   too expensive

11.5
TASK

Name four innovations mentioned in the recording that have helped to move information faster:

1   _____

2   _____

3   _____

4   _____

Which of these has done the most for speeding up the movement of information?

11.6

If the PC has failed to change the way businesses work, then why do so many businesses use them?

Who will need the printed word in the near future?

Visions of Netropolis

Going by the business stories you read these days, you could be forgiven for thinking that the news won't be coming on paper for much longer. When you can have video-on-demand, 500-channel interactive TV, your own custom-designed electronic newspaper culled from daily bulletins around the globe, and hand-held gizmos that manage your phone calls, faxes and electronic mail, who'll need the printed word?

With high-capacity telecomms links now spanning the world, data networks are spreading fast. One phone company has an ad on American TV that talks about 'a highway that you can't see, that links everyone, that goes everywhere'. And almost every US company whose business is telecomms, computers, TV or cable is trying to buy or merge with another one. It's not to give them an excuse to rethink their corporate logo; they're preparing to make the most of the coming revolution.

So, if you've never used the Internet, if you haven't tried a CD-ROM, if you reckon videoconferencing and telecommuting are strictly for technofreaks – think again. The future will belong to those who are at ease with the Net – the technologies by which someone in San Francisco or Szechuan can converse with one, a hundred or a hundred million people at once. Navigating the network will become something you do to find a job, to contact friends, to plot your life.

Attached to the Net, you will be able to work from home, and work for many different employers at once, in a world where white-collar jobs will increasingly be part-time and task-oriented rather than full-time and described by a title. Businesses will need the best information, and that means links to the Net.

When the best jobs aren't advertised, you have to contact the right people to be considered. The place to make the right contacts – an activity long known as 'networking' – will be the Net. In Britain, jobs are 'posted' on the CIX bulletin board – electronic small ads that never get onto paper. The trend can only grow stronger. Businesses, too, will be using global networks more and more to search for background data, to talk to customers and to link offices and computers.

Charles Arthur in Netropolis supplement, New Scientist

11.8 TASK

Think of alternative words or phrases of similar meaning to those in boldface type:

1   Hand-held **gizmos** will manage your phone calls, faxes and electronic mail.
2   If you **reckon** video conferencing and telecommuting are strictly for technofreaks, think again.
3   Businesses, too, will be using **global** networks more and more.
4   Navigating the network will be something you do to **plot** your life.
5   It's not just to give them an excuse to **rethink their corporate logo.**
6   Just look at the **explosion** in the growth of telecommunications services.

11.9

What advantages (for the business as a whole and for the individual worker) does conventional office work offer, compared with the electronically networked professional working from home?

11.10
TASK

Complete the following sentences with the correct form of a suitable phrase from the box below:

Example: Many companies involved in telecommunications
            are preparing to _____ the coming revolution.
            *Many companies involved in telecommunications
            are preparing to **make the most of** the coming
            revolution.*

1   Computerization has _____ many routine clerical
    tasks.
2   We just cannot go on _____ the old-fashioned
    equipment we're using now.
3   If you want to _____ that your enquiry reaches us, why
    don't you put it in writing?
4   Navigating the network will become something you just
    cannot _____ if you want to find a job.
5   The problem with our computer system is that it is
    _____ of equipment from various manufacturers.
6   Looking for too long at computer screens may _____ to
    your eyesight.
7   Obsolete practices will need to be given up to _____
    the future communications revolution.

do without	make do with
do damage	**make the most of**
do away with	make way for
make up	make sure

11.11

In what ways do each of the following present a threat to the
printed word?

■   500 channel interactive TV
■   video-on-demand
■   customized electronic newspapers
■   electronic mail
■   on-screen faxes

Is the future of work too valuable to be left to today's managers?

The future of work: it's all in the mind

Just as individuals are changing their ways of working, so are companies. They too are less tied to time or place, and less reliant on a large, permanent workforce. The mantra now is productivity: getting more from fewer people. Charles Handy, a visiting professor at the London Business School who has written numerous books about the changing shape of work, describes it as the '0.5 x 2 x 3' equation: companies will try to employ half as many full-time staff, pay them twice as much and work them three times as hard.

In such a system, it becomes easier to be a part-time worker. Don't like your employer? Become a consultant, selling your valuable knowledge a bit at a time to different companies. Got the management expertise that a company needs for its latest big project? Sell yourself to them for just as long as it takes.

But is there a wider significance to this change towards part-time work? Handy is convinced that there is, towards a very different society. As he points out, we are oddly short-sighted about how the world changes: 'Every generation perceives itself as justifiably different from its predecessor, but plans as if its successor generation will be the same.' This next generation will be very different. The change here is rather like bursts in evolution where the more effective methods – in business, the more productive ones – triumph over the rest. And technology speeds the process. Many people will lose their outdated jobs almost overnight, and will remain profoundly unemployable, because they lack the variety of skills and mental flexibility to adjust to an economy of ideas which is constantly remaking itself.

Many managers today think it will be easier to run their companies if they resist the changes in technology and society around them. Their problem, says Handy, is that too few ask themselves the question: 'If we were going to reinvent this company from scratch today, would we do it like we are now?' The future, he says, is too valuable to be left to those busy with the present.

Charles Arthur, New Scientist

11.13
TASK

Which factors are explicitly identified in 'The future of work: it's all in the mind' as significant for individual working lives in the future? Select the items that apply:

❏ 1   Detailed knowledge of the superhighway
❏ 2   Varied skills and mental flexibility
❏ 3   Emphasis in companies on productivity and the use of part-time consultants
❏ 4   New legislation on workplace management
❏ 5   Awareness of change in technology and society and of new business methods
❏ 6   Loss of outdated full-time jobs

11.14
TASK

Complete the following sentences by filling in the correct form of a phrasal verb from the box below:

Example: The consultant _____ the offer of a full-time job.
            *The consultant **turned down** the offer of a full-time job.*

1   The company is _____ a research group to find out exactly how work will change in the future.
2   He pressed the wrong key on the keyboard and _____ all the personnel records.
3   Many big companies are _____ full-time staff and replacing them with part-time workers.
4   Commentators like Charles Handy have _____ that every generation is different.
5   The information systems manager felt that the firm's computer technology was _____ the functionality curve in some key capabilities.

wipe out	lay off
point out	**turn down**
set up	fall behind

11.15

What implications would a change from full-time working to reliance on part-time professionals have for your organization or department? Describe your own reactions and the probable reactions of your colleagues.

11.16

> The recorded discussion features comments on the ways in which work will change as networking becomes the norm.
>
> Note these key words and phrases:
>
> | | |
> |---|---|
> | unmanageable | peace dividend |
> | to throw... at... | computerized switching |
> | defence/defense budget | analogy |

**11.17
TASK**

Complete the following sentences:

1   There is a threefold problem with networks: ...
2   In development terms, the computer network today is roughly where...
3   Managers have mainly ensured that networks operate by...
4   The number of telephone operators began to drop ...
5   To make PC networks efficient, we have...

11.18

Will people eventually find using a computer network as easy as holding a telephone conversation?

**11.19
ROLE PLAY**

Two office managers discuss the likely impact of the telecommunications revolution on their work. One (Role **A** – page 123) is excited and optimistic, the other (Role **B** – page 125) is doubtful.

11.20

Make a list of jobs in your business or profession that will become partly or wholly outdated as a result of new business technologies. Explain your selection. Indicate those which could be performed by part-time consultants.

11.21 | Key Vocabulary

analogy	to network, networking
bandwidth	online, on-line
cable news	overnight delivery
CD-ROM	to plot
cellular phone	rugged
commodity	resolution
computer architecture	from scratch
computerized switching	to ship
to cull	short-sighted
custom-designed	stockbroker
deregulation	task-oriented
equation	telecomms
expertise	(telecommunications)
explosion	telecommuting
to fall behind	technofreak
gizmo	to throw... at...
graphics	threshold
'just in time' business	unmanageable
lift-off	unemployable
logo	videoconferencing
lookalike products	white-collar job

Inner and outer space

When you have completed this chapter you should be able to

- discuss scientific views on the nature and applications of consciousness

- discuss the evolution and fate of the cosmos and to express your own views on the forces that govern the earth's environment

- understand and use a range of related terms

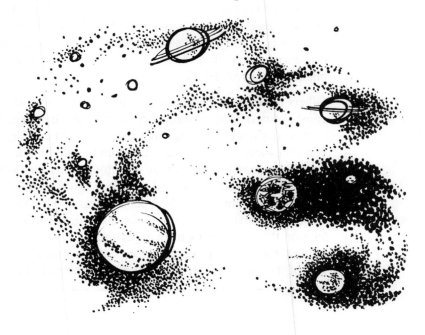

12.1

Warm-up

Describe what you understand by the term 'consciousness'.

Is it possible, under your definition, for plants and lower animals to be conscious?

Are cosmic matter, black holes and neutron stars of any significance to us here on Earth?

12.2
TEXT

How important is consciousness to us? And what is it, anyway?

The elusive conscious mind

Sensibility, working memory and language are all aspects of mind, but they are not the whole thing. What binds them together? What is the conscious mind? It is certainly not the be-all and end-all of complex behaviour. Anyone who has driven along a motorway and suddenly realised he cannot remember the past few miles will recognise this. Nor does partial loss of faculty make a person mindless – although dementias which attack the pre-frontal cortex might.

Hypotheses of how the mind evolved are still vague and contradictory, but they fall into two groups. One interpretation is that consciousness is an epiphenomenon – a side-effect of increased complexity in the brains of higher primates and particularly of people. Such side-effects, known as emergent properties, are just starting to be explored. Some theorists of the origin of life see life itself as an emergent property. They think it suddenly 'switched on' when a network of chemical reactions grew so big that each reaction was able to assist the progress of another. On this theory, brains, and particularly cerebral cortices, passed some threshold of size and complexity during their evolution which allowed the system to feed upon itself and generate the phenomenon now labelled consciousness.

Others believe that consciousness has evolved specifically. In their view, consciousness is an evolutionary advantage which has dictated the brain's complexity rather than the other way round. One widely held theory is that consciousness is a way of dealing with the diplomatic niceties of group living. It is there mainly to answer the question, 'What would I do if I were in the other person's shoes?' Armed with the answer, arrived at by conscious introspection, you can make a better guess at what the other person will actually do next and modify your behaviour accordingly. Some evidence to support this idea comes from experiments on self-awareness. Among primates, at least, the ability to recognise oneself in a mirror is restricted to man and a few of the great apes. Even monkeys see the reflection as a stranger.

The Economist

| 12.3 TASK | *Match the term on the left with the description on the right which best suits it:* |

epiphenomenon	an ongoing process that feeds itself
emergent property	a side effect
dementia	thinking about oneself
cerebral cortex (cortices)	a mental illness
introspection	the outer layer of the brain

12.4 Do we need to fully understand human consciousness before we can develop artificial intelligence?

12.5 TASK

Form adjectives from the nouns in capitals and choose an appropriate noun to complete the sentences:

Example: Consciousness is not the be-all and end-all of COMPLEXITY _____.
Consciousness is not the be-all and end-all of **complex behaviour**.

1 The children were asked to imagine the HYPOTHESIS _____ of running their own schools.
2 London taxi drivers are examined on their THEORY _____ of London's streets as well as on their driving ability.
3 An EXPERIMENT _____ caused major traffic delays during the rush hour.
4 The young man made a CONSCIOUSNESS _____ not to make the same silly mistakes again.
5 Many ORIGIN _____ and paintings were destroyed in the museum fire.

12.6 Much progress has been achieved in the field of intelligent machines. Consider which of the following thinking activities you believe machines are best suited to:

■ playing chess
■ playing poker
■ language translation
■ solving crossword puzzles

12.7

In the recording an expert considers the use of computers to create virtual reality, noting: 'When the computer can simulate virtual space, then you can create almost anything.' What are the implications of this statement?

Note these key words and phrases:

computer games   nightclub
Sega™, Nintendo™   virtual space
games console   to transmit
all walks of life

12.8
TASK

Complete the following sentences:

1   The computer games industry is now...
2   In a virtual night club, you can...
3   Building a virtual world within the computer lets you...
4   If you have the imagination and the money,...
5   You can share the virtual reality experience...

12.9
TASK

Name three industries which you think would be threatened by the scenario described in the recording and three which you think would benefit:

	Threatened	Would Benefit
1	_____	_____
2	_____	_____
3	_____	_____

Can our consciousness extend to comprehending the way the cosmos will end? Will the universe finish in a big chill or a big fireball?

A matter of matter

Prepare yourself for the big chill. No, this is not a weather forecast. It is a prediction about the fate of the cosmos. According to some astronomers, the universe is going to end not with a bang, but with a whimper – and a very cold one at that. 'It looks as if there is simply a lack of matter in the universe to stop it expanding,' says Dr Paul Murdin, organizer of the 1994 European and National Astronomy Meeting in Edinburgh. 'The heavens are going to continue flying apart forever.'

Scientists are, at last, closing in on answers to some of the most fundamental questions. Having shown that our universe erupted in a Big Bang 15 billion years ago, astronomers had been left to grapple with the implications of this extraordinary explosive genesis. How could the thin soup have coalesced into this lumpy cosmos of galaxies and stars?

And then there have been questions about the amount of matter. Most evidence suggests there is much more than is visible to astronomers – and that has implications that touch on the ultimate fate of our universe. If the universe contains only a limited amount of extra atoms, neutrons or quarks, it will continue to fly apart – forever. If, however, it contains a great deal of matter, the combined gravitational forces of its constituent parts will eventually drag it back in a weird re-running of its expansion. In the end, stars and galaxies will plunge together and be consumed in a fireball. But which scenario is correct?

The former, says Dr Murdin. The cosmos will expand without limit, its stars slowly fizzling out until a grim entropic chill permeates the cosmos. His evidence comes from comparing various studies of the cosmic microwave background, the leftover echoes of the Big Bang. In 1992, Nasa's Cosmic Background Explorer satellite showed variations in this field, the first signs that matter was beginning to coalesce about 300,000 years after the creation of the cosmos.

Since then, scientists have studied these ripples and analysed their radio emissions, while instruments carried by hot air balloons have studied other wavelengths. 'By combining this data, we get a much fuller picture of the early "bumps" in the universe – and also of how much matter there is,' says Dr Murdin.

Robin McKie, The Observer

12.11
TASK

In which paragraphs of 'A matter of matter' do you find the following?

1 two different predictions about the ultimate fate of the universe
2 why the universe will stop expanding
3 a word which describes the unavailability of energy in the universe
4 the plural of datum
5 the approximate age of the universe

12.12
TASK

Form one sentence from each pair, using the gerund:

Example: It looks as if there is simply a lack of matter in the universe/this causes it to continue expanding
*It looks as if there is simply a lack of matter in the universe, **causing** it to continue expanding.*

1 Stars and galaxies might collapse/this will create a huge fireball that will consume everything
2 There was a Big Bang 15 billion years ago/all the matter and energy in the universe was exploded
3 Evidence suggests that there is more matter than is actually visible to astronomers/this raises the issue of the ultimate fate of the universe
4 If the universe contains a lot of matter, gravitational forces will pull back the stars and galaxies/they will eventually destroy them

12.13

The space programme and astronomy have benefited humanity in many practical ways. For each benefit listed below, think of a space-related project or discipline which has produced it:

- non-stick frying pans
- accurate weather reports
- better understanding of nuclear power
- medical research in new areas
- improved radio communications

**12.14
ROLE PLAY**

A radio interviewer (Role **A** – page 123) questions an astronomer (Role **B** – page 125) who believes in the 'big chill' theory.

**12.15
TASK**

Which one verb can you use before all the nouns or noun phrases in the box?

under control	under lock and key
an eye on	their heads above water
the peace	their distance

Now complete the sentences with full phrases from the box:

1   The tourists' passports were _____ in the hotel safe during their holiday.
2   A number of military personnel were sent to the area of conflict to _____ during the elections.
3   The photographers were asked to _____ from the president during his tour of the city.
4   The footballer had trouble _____ his nerves _____ before he took the penalty kick.
5   Would you _____ my dog while I go to the post office?
6   It was difficult for them to _____ after the third child was born and the man lost his job.

12.16
TEXT

Can 'correct' scientific opinion ever admit the possibility of a mysterious interaction between living organisms and the environment?

Do living things regulate the planet?

James Lovelock's Gaia hypothesis – a liberating concept for many environmentalists and natural scientists – is named after the Greek goddess personifying the earth. It is based on the observation that living organisms help to shape the fundamental features of our planet's surface, establishing and maintaining the chemical balance of the atmosphere and the oceans. Furthermore, it postulates that this process is carried on in such a way as to regulate the planet in the general interest of living things.

Papers by Lovelock and his supporters have shown how algæ in the seas might control air temperature above the ocean by seeding the clouds. Harvard's Dick Holland, a specialist in the history of oxygen in the atmosphere, sees living things as part of a control mechanism that has kept atmospheric oxygen levels within 50 percent of present values for the past 300 million years. Others suggest that living organisms determine the rate of weathering of rocks, a main driving force of the earth's cooling process through continental drift.

But the Gaia hypothesis has stirred up a good deal of controversy in the scientific community. The concept of a unifying theory for the earth – a whole greater than the sum of its parts – is one that many scientists find hard to entertain, while the idea of an active planetary environment offends those environmentalists who cherish their view of a passive, fragile earth. Others, while readily accepting the notion of cells cooperating within an organism, take issue with the idea of cooperation between organisms in the planet's general interest. Would such a process not require a central, coordinating intelligence?

The essence of the debate may turn on a question of terminology. Lovelock has favoured the idea of a process of 'regulation', while Holland and others prefer to speak of the 'modulation' of the environment. More recently, aware that scientific orthodoxy is likely to be sceptical of a theory named for a Greek goddess, Lovelock seems to have modified his position. 'Biology doesn't control everything,' he told a 1994 Oxford meeting. 'Gaia is about system control, and the biosphere exerts a strong influence.'

**12.17
TASK**

Which of these statements accurately reflect items of information given in 'Do living things regulate the planet?' Select the items that apply:

❑ 1   Lovelock realizes that his fellow-scientists might take issue with a theory named for a goddess.

❑ 2   Lately Lovelock has started to talk of 'influence' instead of 'control'.

❑ 3   Most scientists would readily accept the idea of a central coordinating intelligence.

❑ 4   Dick Holland thinks that oxygen levels have been maintained without the help of living organisms.

❑ 5   Some environmentalists believe in a passive planet and cannot accept the idea of interactivity among organisms.

❑ 6   Many scientists see the Gaia hypothesis as a liberating concept because it frees them from a somewhat rigid orthodoxy.

12.18

If we accept Lovelock's hypothesis as true, we no longer need to be so concerned about the effects of acid rain, ozone depletion or desertification. Nature is capable of healing itself. Discuss.

12.19

Find a newspaper report or magazine article that deals with 'inner or outer space'. Summarize it and be prepared to answer questions.

12.20 | # Key Vocabulary

abrupt	hypothesis
algæ	modulation
all walks of life	neutron star
anomaly	orthodoxy
the be-all and end-all of...	in the other person's shoes
biosphere	to plump for...
black hole	to postulate
cerebral cortex/cortices	primate
to coalesce	self-aware
conducive to...	
conscious, consciousness	sensibility
contradictory	side-effect
control mechanism	spiral
dementia	symmetry
discrepancy	to take issue with...
entropic	to transmit
epiphenomenon	to turn on...
to exert an influence	unifying
faculty	virtual space
globule	weathering
gravitational forces	working memory

Role A

1.16

As the sales director of J.X. Windeal, a large European civil engineering contractor, you are anxious to secure more export business for your company. You have therefore invested a good deal of money in setting up overseas bases with a view to winning large contracts funded by World Bank loans to developing countries. You have been invited to take part in a television panel discussion on the developing world. You wish to defend the use of Western technologies in developing economies against the arguments of environmentalists who see the use of intermediate technologies as the best way of improving the health and welfare of local populations. You genuinely believe that Western technology offers the best way for developing economies to advance and to become commercially competitive, but you are anxious not to reveal the secret agreements you have made with leading politicians in some of these economies.

2.16

You are a Brazilian politician representing a constituency in which the São Francisco Valley irrigation project is situated. You are one of the chief advocates of irrigation and fertilization and you staked much of your reputation on the benefits that the project would provide for the local people. You are now receiving reports from conservationist bodies claiming that the irrigation project is damaging the local environment, reducing bird life and harming plant species. You believe firmly that the welfare of the local population must be considered above other priorities and you feel that the conservationists' claims are exaggerated. You are also aware that your own power and influence will be forever diminished if the conservationist argument prevails. You are about to defend your position in a confrontation with a leader of the environmentalist lobby.

7.15

As a government representative, you are visiting a small coastal town in your constituency to talk about a proposed law that will establish temporary fishing quotas in an effort to halt overfishing of the local waters. You are expecting the townspeople to be heavily opposed to the new measure, especially as most of them earn their livings either directly or indirectly from commercial fishing. The mood in the town is grim. After a brief boom a decade ago, the annual catches have since been drastically reduced and many locals have been forced out of business. While the local fishermen lay the blame for overfishing on the large commercial fishing companies that they feel are trespassing in 'their' waters, you realize that some of the responsibility lies with the local fishermen themselves who, despite indications of a dwindling fish supply, continued to increase productivity in search of profits. You are about to start the meeting.

9.9

You are a charity manager based in a large Western city. You are responsible for preparing and distributing information on your organization's work in developing countries, where it helps local communities to set up health care and improvement schemes. You are conscious that in times of economic recession people in the industrial countries have less money to spare for charity donations. You are therefore considering spending some of your money on an advertising campaign designed to bring the organization to the public's notice and to encourage them to keep up their donations. Your contacts in an advertising agency have indicated that they will be willing to offer you preferential rates. However, you expect some opposition to the proposal from your colleague B, who feels that the charity should lobby lawmakers and badger government ministers for assistance with funding.

9.16

You are a manager in a small manufacturing company based in a medium-sized town. You are involved in a number of local community initiatives, including a national recycling scheme which is now being implemented by the local council. You are aware of the good publicity that can result from your company's perceived involvement in green issues and you genuinely feel that the cause is worthwhile. However, you are also conscious of the opposition to the official policies which is now being voiced by an environmentalist group for whom B is a prominent local spokesman. You are about to attend a public meeting at which B will attack your policies, demanding a more radical and comprehensive approach. B's views have a measure of support in the town but you feel that his/her arguments are driven more by a desire for power than by any serious concern for the local environment. You are also apprehensive about the increase in local taxation that will be needed to fund B's proposals if they win approval.

11.19

You are a human resource manager in a large public-sector organization. You have begun to take an interest in information technology and you recently followed a course in the use of computer spreadsheets and databases. You have put some proposals on information systems and network development to your head of section and these have been quite well received. You realize that these schemes will need funding and you are willing to implement them on a gradual basis. However, in the meeting you are about to attend you expect some opposition from B, a financial manager with whom you are anxious to discuss these matters. You suspect that B is jealous of the attention your proposals have won and that he/she feels that systems development should be handled by the financial department.

12.14

You are a radio journalist working for a leading news-and-chat station in your country's capital city. You host a weekday morning discussion programme in which personalities from the arts and the scientific world talk about current issues and matters of interest. You are about to interview a prominent astronomer (B) who believes firmly in the 'big chill' theory and claims that the cosmos will go on expanding until its stars fizzle out. You do not really want to interview B; firstly, you think the big chill topic is depressing; secondly, you have not had time to read up on the subject; thirdly, you find astronomers a bit of a bore and you have agreed to do the interview only because B is an old college friend of the radio station's managing director.

Role B

1.16

You are a committed aid worker with substantial experience in a number of Asian and African countries. You have been invited to take part in a television panel discussion on the developing world. You wish to attack the use of Western technologies in developing economies, advocating the use of intermediate technologies as the best way of improving the health and welfare of local populations. You believe that a measure of Western technology may help some developing economies to advance but you are anxious to ensure that their environments are not harmed by rapid and uncontrolled industrialization. You also have evidence that the directors of J.X. Windeal, a large European civil engineering contractor – a representative of whom (A) will be taking part in the TV discussion – have made secret agreements with some politicians in certain developing economies to further their interests in these areas.

2.16

You are an environmentalist teaching at a university in the part of Brazil where the São Francisco Valley irrigation project is situated. You are one of the chief advocates of conservation and the progress of the project has caused you much concern. You have published articles claiming that the irrigation project is damaging the local environment, reducing bird life and harming plant species. You believe firmly that, although the welfare and prosperity of the local population must be considered, their environment will be irreparably damaged if the irrigation project is not strictly controlled. You believe that the government should urgently allocate funds for the protection of the landscape and its natural species. You are about to defend your position in a confrontation with a local politician (A) who is in a position to benefit from the expansion of the irrigation project.

7.15

You are a fisherman, earning your livelihood from the sea like your parents and grandparents before you. When you took over the fishing business from your father, there was plenty of work for all the local fishermen and you felt confident enough in your future to invest in a new boat and more modern equipment, thereby considerably increasing your productivity. Yet, over the past decade, many large commercial fishing companies have started working in the area and the increased competition has finally resulted in severe overfishing of the local waters. You are attending a meeting in which your government representative (A) is talking about a proposed law that will establish temporary fishing quotas. While you realize overfishing is a problem, you feel the blame lies with the large fishing companies; they should be banned from fishing in the area so that the local fishermen can continue to earn their livelihoods as they have done for centuries.

9.9

You work for a large Western charity. You help your colleague A to prepare and distribute information on your organization's work in developing countries, where it helps local communities to set up health care and improvement schemes. You are conscious that in times of economic recession people in the industrial countries have less money to spare for charity donations. You feel that the charity should lobby lawmakers and badger government ministers for assistance with funding. You are strongly against A's view that money should be spent on an advertising campaign designed to bring the organization to the public's notice and to encourage them to keep up their donations. You are aware that advertising agencies may be willing to offer preferential rates but you feel that whatever funds are available should go to help developing communities to train their people in health care and that the charity's administrative and advertising costs should be minimized. You raise this issue with A.

9.16

You are a genuinely committed environmentalist. You belong to a regional pressure group which is trying to get local authorities to adopt radical and comprehensive approaches to recycling priorities instead of the official scheme now being implemented, which you think is a token gesture made by local bureaucrats and industrialists – including A, a prominent representative of local business – to avoid more generous investment in ecological policies. You are about to attend a public meeting at which you will attack A's policies, demanding a more radical and comprehensive approach. Your views have a measure of support in the town but you feel that A will be able to play on the fears of townspeople about the increase in local taxation that may be needed to fund your proposals if you win the day.

11.19

You are a financial manager in the large public-sector organization where A works as a human resource manager. You have studied A's proposals for upgrading the computer systems in your organization. You oppose them because you think the expenditure required to implement them will be excessive. However, you also regard him/her as politically naive and feel that his/her claimed expertise in information technology is shallow and ill-informed. In fact, you have heard from informal contacts that A's performance in a recent course on computer applications was less than satisfactory. You feel that systems development should be handled by your own department. You are about to put your case to A at an interdepartmental meeting.

12.14

You are an eminent astronomer with a strong belief in the 'big chill' theory: you believe that the cosmos will go on expanding until its stars fizzle out. At very short notice you have agreed to take part in a morning radio discussion with A, a journalist with a reputation for a bullying and impatient manner. You are convinced that the fate of the universe deserves the attention of the public at large and you are therefore anxious that the interview should go well. However, you wish to put A in his/her place. You are also feeling a bit impatient because the managing director of the radio station, an old college friend of yours, has invited you out to lunch at one of the best restaurants in town. You are about to start the radio interview.

Transcripts

The following transcripts are literal representations of the unscripted words of the speakers involved. Any extemporaneous speech often involves the use of sentence fragments, and even grammatical and stylistic errors. We have not attempted to delete these from the transcripts.

Chapter One: Technology and development

Audio One (1.9)

Speaker 1	Why are you keen on what are called tradeable permits in pollution?
Speaker 2	Well, it's a way for us as a world society to find out how much CO_2 the world can bear, and deal fairly with the problem. You give companies permits to pollute, and these permits are tradeable by companies so that there is an incentive. So the developing countries pollute more for the time being, then as they move away from those technologies, they sell the permits to others and get cash benefits for not polluting. How would you feel about that, Alan?
Speaker 1	Well, I'm not sure it's realistic. How can the poorer countries afford it, and meanwhile, the richer countries can press ahead with the newer less polluting industrial processes.
Speaker 3	But that's how the issue of aid would work. Less developed countries can use aid from the developed world to buy these permits and then as they increase their income and their national product, they can trade on again.
Speaker 2	The problem is not just the access to aid, it seems to me, but trade barriers like the European Common Agricultural Policy. I think we need to find ways for developing countries to trade in what they do best without having to pollute their own environment, instead of, for example, being given high-quality grain that the local farmers can't compete with.
Speaker 3	But wait a minute. There's clearly an argument which says it's actually more efficient to move pollution from developed to less developed countries. The developed countries already have very high levels of pollution. Any additional pollution that they create will be much more difficult to deal with, and cost much more to get rid of, than if it's shifted.
Speaker 1	What you are saying is, if the developed countries stop polluting, at the level they have now, and if the less developed countries take that pollution on, given the very low level they have now, the costs and difficulties of getting rid of it are much lower.
Speaker 3	I think that's what I'm saying, yes.

Chapter Two: Fuel, power and natural resources

Audio One (2.2)

Speaker 1   Can you tell me a little bit about the cases involving connections between power-lines and cancer?

Speaker 2   Well, the whole thing's been brewing for about 15 years now. In 1979 there was a epidemiological study performed in Denver, Colorado, and there was some suggestion from this study that children from families that live near power-lines were more susceptible to leukemia than a control group that didn't. But not a lot was done about the study because the assessment of exposure to electric and magnetic fields was not very exact. The assessment was made on the basis of a visual observation of the number of power-lines and the thickness of power-lines going to each of the houses, and the estimate of distance was in the 50's of metres from the houses.

The electricity companies contested that this wasn't a fair estimate of exposure or risk because the amount of power to the lines could vary – it wasn't totally dependent on the size of the lines or indeed the distance from the houses. Various different things could shield houses and people in the houses from electric and magnetic fields.

There have also been several more studies done since then, none of which showed a large increased risk of leukemia from power-lines. Some showed what might be construed as a small increase in risk.

But there are many criticisms of the studies. Generally, the studies are far too small and deal with very few cases, so it's difficult to draw conclusions. Furthermore, when looking at epidemiological studies like this, you've got to be very aware of the confounding factors. If you start to look at factors like electric and magnetic fields and their relative risk with something like leukemia, you also have to look at other possible factors, some of which might be things like the sociological or the socioeconomic position of the people in the houses. Generally, poorer people tend to live nearer to high-voltage power lines down to substations and so on. You also have to look at the traffic density in the area. Generally a lot of power-lines follow major traffic routes. All these confounding factors have to be taken into account when establishing an increased risk.

Audio Two (2.6)

Speaker 1   More sophisticated studies examine the effects of magnetic and electrical fields on cells grown in a laboratory. Have these studies come any closer to establishing a link?

Speaker 2   The effects that may or may not occur, if they do occur, will be very small and so they have to be shielded from whatever background effects there are due to the other stresses on cells, things like mechanical stresses – moving the cells – or the temperature at which they're maintained, or how long since the cells were fed. All of these things will affect your measurement of any stimulation which may be there due to electric or magnetic fields.

So you have to remove these background causes. Now there are several ways of doing that. The commonest way is to have a control group of cells which are treated in exactly the same way as the exposed or potentially stimulated set, but which of course aren't actually stimulated. So you do all of your manipulations simultaneously on a control and an experimental set and then make the same measurements at the end and you see if you have any increase in whatever you are measuring in your exposed set over your controls.

But the effects are, again, so small in this field that it is often necessary to go a step further and perform experiments in which you have no exposed set. You merely have a Control Group 1 and a Control Group 2 and you look at variation within or between your control groups and compare that with variation between your experimental and your control groups and you see if there is an increase in variation between your exposed control groups and then you can begin to infer that there may be some effect. Ultimately there are so many extra factors which can contribute to changes in the cells that it is very difficult to prove for legal purposes that there's any link between these magnetic fields and increased incidence of cancer.

Chapter Three: Using technology

Audio One (3.2)

Speaker 1   Most of us know bar codes from the retail area. When we do our shopping we see all the funny codes on the goods we are buying, and that's probably where today bar codes are mostly used.

However, there's a new development coming up, because if you look at a bar code as it is on your groceries, it's basically what we call a linear bar code. You need, in order to get information about the product you are buying, you have to look it up in a file. So basically what the bar code gives you as information is just the product number and then when you get to the checkout lane in your supermarket, what happens is in the checkout lane they will read the bar code, and the system will look up in a datafile to see what the name of the product is and what the price is. At the end of the checkout it adds up what you have bought for today and you pay and things are all okay.

So that's the basic use of a bar code, what we call a linear bar code, and basically it's like a license plate, you have to look up in a database in order to see what is behind the product number.

The new development in bar codes is they become two-dimensional. So you don't have to look up in a datafile to see what is actually behind the bar code number but all the information is contained in the bar code. That's called portable datafiles which means basically you have – the bar code is a datafile in itself.

Basically what it means is that even if you have not access to a datafile or computer, you can get all the information about the product. In today's portable datafiles you can actually store up to 2,000 characters just in a small bar code, and you can also chain different bar codes together, so basically you can have as much information contained in several bar codes as you want.

So really what it means is that if, for example, you have applications where you have no way of getting access to a datafile, like for example, take waste material, for example, drums with poisonous waste. If a lorry with those waste materials is having an accident, you need immediately to know what type of poison you have in the lorry and you don't have access to what you say a datafile but you need all the information and you read this portable datafile bar code and in one go you can have all the information about what to do with the waste material, how to clean it off, is it dangerous for the people who are actually around?, etc., etc.

Chapter Four: The world of IT systems

Audio One (4.2)

Speaker 1   Open systems means many things to many people but I guess the word "open" really means – a definition I would use is that... Can you change your purchase based on the fact that you can migrate from one system to another easily without undue cost penalties or time penalties? The reason why that's important is it stimulates competition.

The hardware and software vendors in the industry now have to compete on either price or functionality because they can't lock the customer into being dependent on one proprietory environment. In the old days of computing, it was always the case if you bought one vendor's system you were almost forced to stay with that vendor forever and that became very, very difficult to justify because that vendor may fall behind the performance curve or the price curve or the functionality curve and then you felt frustration about being locked in. So this thing has mushroomed for about the last 8 years. It actually was started probably about 15 - 20 years ago and it has taken that length of time to mature. But really, flexibility of purchase, which means that the vendors have to compete, and therefore the prices drop, the functionality goes up and the whole market is stimulated.

Audio Two (4.13)

Speaker 1   Many people believe that chips are not a very important part of computers these days because customers don't buy chips they buy solutions and the chip set is simply at the very lowest level of this thing. It's like saying which tyres do I have on a car when you're buying a car? In some ways you don't care but actually tyres are very important in terms of the performance of the car and chips are very important in terms of the performance of the computer.

A better analogy of course is with our car engine. Now one of the problems with chips is that it comes down to price and performance and functionality, and as you add performance and functionality, the cost to manufacturer escalates astronomically, so each new generation of chip technology requires probably a doubling of the investment or more in order of magnitude change and so it's becoming very, very difficult to afford it. So that means that you have to have a very broad market and you have to have very powerful investors with deep pockets to make this happen.

So what's happening is there are fewer and fewer technologies around and in the longer term, there will be even more – even fewer of those. The bottom line is that there's going to be a big confrontation between a very small number of American manufacturers and maybe one or two Japanese manufacturers as well. The net result of that is that we will see further wars – price wars and so on and we will see escalation, by the way, of what I might call performance characteristics – the chips will get faster and faster, cheaper and cheaper, smaller and smaller, and probably one or two brands will begin to dominate the market.

In principle, having more choice is always better as we discussed in open systems. The whole thing about open systems is its freedom of choice and actually there's a reverse trend here. In open systems, the trend is to have more availability and functionality at the software level in this business. The trend is the other way in the hardware which is to have less availability of choice because of the economics which I've just been discussing. So in some ways, no, it's not a good idea that you have rationalisation of the industry into a few large cartels – but in practice that's the only way forward because the costs are just astronomical.

Now I do believe, though, that what will happen is we'll see a huge diversity of hardware types of product on the market, which maybe we'll discuss when we discuss multimedia, because when we look at the hardware types around, we'll also see other types of hardware coming into play based on maybe television sets or telephones or whatever, and there'll be a convergence of these things and that will actually stimulate creativity and divergence as well.

Chapter Five: Technology and everyday life

Audio One (5.2)

Speaker 1   The higher the bandwidth the better because you can get higher quality pictures, more channels and everything else, and the higher the bandwidth, the more it costs. But just to give you an example, video on demand is something that's talked about a lot in this industry, that means that you sit at home and you can dial up from somewhere in central – centre, data centre – any film perhaps that you ever wanted to watch in your life and you can do it a repeated number of times.

Now the technology for that is actually very simple, it's just your television set plus a little black box of tricks which costs you maybe £300 and away you go. Now the trouble with that is that the vendors of that would have to provide you with a video at less than it would cost you to walk down your High Street and buy it from the local video store which is about £3 a night roughly. And frankly it would possibly cost them £10 to deliver to you at least, if not more than that, so they're going to have to figure out how to make that cost-effective and, by the way, you can probably buy a video and a pizza for less than £10 and so then it comes to the question of what is the real demographics of this and that's the real big question.

There's lots of interest, lots of hype, lots of investment which would fail because just the demographics don't work, but there will be some applications which really take off like wildfire and I don't believe anybody knows what they are yet but they definitely will be there because as we build the so-called 'super-data highway' – and it will be built – eventually we'll find that we can actually start using that. And I liken this to the days back in the early 1900s when we had a motor car and there were no motorways, perhaps not even very many A roads, all we were doing was actually tarmacking country tracks; that's where we are right now with this stuff and you imagine, 90 years on, we've got motorways everywhere and so on, we will eventually get to have motorways for this industry as well, but right now we're probably just exploring country lanes with a bit of tarmac.

Audio Two (5.14)

Speaker 1   Well, it is certainly not an easy task to explain what objects are. But if we look back over the last 10 years, the programmers were trained to think in a procedural way, which is a way of thinking that aims to define functions within programmes and programme in a computer-based language which is not a natural language for human beings. Object is an entirely new way of approaching programming concepts. It helps programmers and people to model real-world entities when designing systems meeting their business needs. So the benefits of objects are enormous.

Firstly, they impose structure modularity, they help to re-use existing components because building object-based applications is like constructing a complex Lego out of the individual components, and more importantly it helps every individual involved in the whole process of building object-based applications to think in more intuitive, human ways of thinking, looking at the real-world entities rather than looking at a difficult language that computers used to use in the past.

Chapter Six: Health issues

Audio One (6.2)

Speaker 1   Can you tell me a little bit about the human genome project?

Speaker 2   The human genome project is an attempt to establish the exact sequence of all genes within the human gene make-up. Within every cell in your body you have a genetic blueprint for the whole organism. This is made up of a material called DNA (deoxyribonucleic acid). This DNA is organized in long chains and there are four different genetic letters that each of these base positions can have – either A, C, G or T – and these things are organized rather like beads on a piece of string and they spell out a code, and your cells read this code and make proteins, enzymes, biological catalysts according to the sequence of letters on this code. Now each of the groups of a piece of code that makes a single enzyme is known as a gene and that corresponds to a specific physical area on your cell's DNA.

The genome programme operates at several different levels. At its most basic level the object is to work out the exact sequence of all these A's, C's, G's and T's throughout the whole of the DNA of a particular organism – humans. But there are other higher levels that the genome project may operate at. As I've said, these letters are organized into groups known as genes, each of which codes for a particular enzyme that does a particular job within the body. Now the importance of the human genome project is to work out the sequence of these genes – where they lie within your various chromosomes. A chromosome is just one string of these DNA beads. And once we have an idea of where genes lie within the human chromosomes and what their normal DNA sequence should be, we are in a position where we can do a lot of diagnostic work.

Speaker 1	So once the human genome project is completed, say in the next ten years or so, what possible uses would it be put to? And are there any dangers about knowing so much about the human geneological make-up?
Speaker 2	Well, let's deal with the advantages first. As a diagnostic tool it will be very useful. A lot of diseases have either genetic causes or people have genetic predispositions to a particular disease.
	A classic genetic disease is cystic fibrosis. This is caused by a single chain, often in one of these bases – A's, C's, G's or T's – which causes the production of a defective enzyme and so the individual with this cystic fibrosis mutation develops cystic fibrosis. It's generally young European males, and they normally die in their early 20's.
	Now, what has recently been done is that the cystic fibrosis gene itself has been sequenced, that is the mutation has been identified and we are now in a position where we can make copies of this gene that do work – normal copies – and actually we are now able to introduce these genes back into the individuals who suffer from cystic fibrosis. And in doing that, by reintroducing a gene that works, you should be able to cure the disease, and some progress has been made on that front.
	So this is called gene therapy and could potentially be in the next 10 or 20 years a very powerful medical tool, but of course with these advantages come possible disadvantages. We all know the story of Frankenstein's monster, and there are people who would argue that reintroducing a functional cystic fibrosis gene also opens the way for reintroducing lots of other types of gene; for example, there is a possibility that we may identify a gene which is correlated with people with higher intelligence, so should we somehow try and reintroduce that gene into people? Or genes for blue eyes or brown eyes. Or genes for fair hair. Or perhaps even genes for skin colour. So there is a lot of concern that the information that we gain from the human genome project will not be used to introduce physical or mental attributes that people normally wouldn't be born with.

Audio Two (6.9)

Speaker 1   Quite apart from the sort of designer body type of issues, aren't there also some insurance and legal type issues where they say if you got hold of a strand of someone's hair you could get absolutely all the information about them that you could possibly want, such as if they do have a predisposition towards cancer or heart disease or something. Is that actually going to be feasible? Obviously from an insurance point of view, people wouldn't insure you if they thought you were going to die at the age of 50.

Speaker 2   Absolutely. It's becoming increasingly obvious that many diseases, particularly if we take diseases such as cancer, a very wide ranging disease, lots of different causes, lots of different effects – but particularly cancer and heart disease – have with them a very high incidence of genetic predisposition and so it's also true to say that if we could develop diagnostic tests for these particular dispositions, then with a sample of someone's DNA you could work out whether they had a predisposition to these particular diseases. And I think that the insurance policy argument is something that could potentially become a problem, and legislation is probably needed to prevent this.

Speaker 1   One last question obviously is that... the fact that you can actually discover all you need to know about someone's later health life just from a strand of hair, coupled with the fact that you can cure any genetic defect, surely seems to me to be kind of a counter-argument to make the whole insurance issue rather negligible because if you find out someone's going to have heart disease later in life they can just immediately cure it and then be insurable.

Speaker 2   Well that's an interesting argument. What I didn't say is that it isn't necessarily true that by getting the sequence of someone's DNA you could work out whether they will die of heart disease at 50 or whether they will die of cancer at 60. You can merely say that statistically they have an increased incidence, or an increased probability of incidence of a particular disease. But of course most of these diseases – cancer, heart disease and so on – aren't purely genetic diseases. You may have a genetic predisposition to a disease but equally as important, or possibly a lot more important, are the environmental factors that you are subjected to, things like chemical carcinogens, cancer causing agents, such as benzene, or lack of exercise which certainly gives an increased risk of heart disease, or diet – high cholesterol diets, high fat diets.

Chapter Seven: Green issues

Audio One (7.2)

Speaker 1   The fuel consumption on these aircraft is really quite phenomenal. In training jets alone, very small training jets will use about a ton of fuel every thirty minutes. A tanker will carry a hundred tons of fuel, and often on exercises, these will get airborne, completely heavy with a hundred tons of fuel, be told to land again and will dump it all, and that will be dumped preferably over the sea or over the land, but either way, there is quite a huge pollution issue there.

Also the way budgetary systems work in the military, it often means that if you don't use your fuel allowance by the end of the financial year, you lose it next year. So, by the time March gets around, everybody gets airborne, and spends time just flying, just burning fuel, just so that you can have your fuel allowance next year. So both those two things are really quite damaging to the environment in general.

Speaker 2   Now you mentioned that often they'll dump the fuel over the ocean if there is any sort of a problem. Does the military have any sort of clean-up exercise when that happens?

Speaker 1   No, when you dump it, you are just basically turning quite a large density tap, and it just falls out of the back of the aircraft and just like rain that will disperse into droplets or mist, it will just fall down and hopefully, to scatter over the countryside quite widely.

But there have been examples of people dumping things when they shouldn't, for example, there was a Buccaneer aircraft, which is a strike attack aircraft, and they were practising with troops on the field, pretending that they were being bombarded by chemicals and this aircraft was due to drop these chemicals over these troops to make sure they were wearing the proper equipment and it didn't damage them. The aircraft had to turn back because of weather and it dumped these chemicals over a car showroom forecourt and it stripped all the paint on all the cars, so that was a big bill. But, David, I understand that you had some experience in the oil industry.

Speaker 2   Yes, and your story about dumping fuel over the ocean, set off a memory in me because that sort of problem is very significant in the oil industry when you have accidents. I remember at one point, I was up on a field visit, up in Northern Canada, and I was at a fairly major gas collection plant. It had probably about a hundred different wells connected to it and had a pipeline heading south which met up with one of the major pipelines. Now this sort of intermediary pipeline, the day that I was there, had a pressure blowout. Part of the pipe basically burst, and it burst at a point where it was in the middle of a river, so you have two sorts of pollution when that sort of thing happens. One is you get the immediate gas which is in the pipeline at the point of the break is suddenly dispersing right out through the water and we had a fairly major fish kill off at that point which was rather damaging because it was also during the breeding season, but once the gas collection plant finds out about this, they have to shut down, basically close the valves to the main pipeline, but they still have all of the gas coming in from all of their wells, and at that point all they can basically do is flare it off, which means you light a match, put it to the gas and away it burns out of midair, and the gas when it is coming out of the wells is often quite polluted, (well, polluted is probably the wrong word to use – but it has lots of contaminants in it) and when you have to do a flare, you're basically flaring it off with no filters, nothing else, it's just burning straight into the air and unfortunately at this point, there is not much that technology has done to solve those sorts of problems. There is not much they can do when you have a pressure burn-out.

Audio Two (7.16)

Speaker 1 Now, I believe that any company, large or small, should be able to find simple, efficient, environment-conscious projects which will harness the enthusiasm of their employees, their customers, and their suppliers. Today, let me mention just three: energy efficiency, water management, and product recycling. And I'll show you the bottom line benefit to IBM UK. Already, simple policies on energy conservation are saving IBM UK hundreds of thousands of pounds a year. For instance, introducing dark computer rooms, that is having no lights on in computer areas which are visited only rarely by engineers, is saving thirty-thousand pounds per year. Modifying chiller controls and installing heat reclaim facilities is saving seventy-thousand pounds a year. And installing energy-efficient lighting, simply changing the types of tube that we use is saving us twenty-thousand pounds a year. In total, these, and other measures, have added up to a saving of over five hundred thousand pounds a year for the last five years.

We are also saving money and reducing health risks through our new comprehensive water management standard, which incorporates best practice for the design, operation and maintenance of water systems. An audit showed that we were buying more chemicals than we needed to treat our water supply, as a result we've reduced the amount and thus saved money and reduced health risks at the same time. The new standard, which covers drinking water, and supplies for cafeterias and air conditioners, has already saved us twenty thousand pounds a year at our headquarters in Portsmouth, and now similar savings are being investigated in many of our other locations. Meanwhile, for some years, we have been operating a "cradle to grave" approach for our computing equipment throughout all our offices and sites, collecting equipment that's no longer required and recycling it. Last year some fifteen hundred tons of obsolete internal equipment was recovered, and we increased the recycling rate to 80 percent by weight.

Let me now turn to the second consideration: avoiding the negative impact of environmental legislation. Already, new requirements are being put in place here in the UK, and, as we have seen very recently, the European Commission is stepping up its efforts to monitor member countries' compliance with its various directives. Here, the impact can be both direct and indirect.

At the most basic level, failure to meet regulatory standards will clearly carry with it financial penalties. But equally, all the evidence suggests that those who have to scramble to meet the requirements at the last minute will find that the costs of doing so far exceed a properly planned programme put in place in good time. And, of course, these are only the direct effects. The impact on company image, of failure to comply, can carry with it huge costs, as several companies have learned the hard way. Nor, I suggest, will this situation remain static.

I was in the United States recently discussing environmental issues. Over there the idea that the polluter pays is well accepted. If your company pollutes a river, for instance, you would expect to be fined. But the new twist that is now emerging in many states is that the fines are increasingly in proportion to the company's financial status and size rather than to the scale of damage caused. Thus a multi-million pound international company can face massive fines for what, of itself, may be a relatively minor incident. And of course, such events in turn have an uncanny knack of finding their way on to the front pages of the newspapers, creating a perception that can tarnish a company's image for a long time.

Chapter Eight: Predicting the future

Audio One (8.7)

Speaker 1   I've been spending the past year working part-time for a design consultancy, and their brief to me was to develop a business process for them which would help them anticipate trends and anticipating these trends have been all aspects of business, of design, of products, of what consumers would want tomorrow. What I came up with was a system which involved four aspects.

One of it was just straightforward consumer research, a second aspect was getting creative groups of industry experts and academics and people with particular learning, in whichever field they were trying to anticipate the trend in. The third aspect was a system which was developed by a woman in America called Faith Popcorn, and her firm Brain Reserve, which is gaining some notoriety now, and that involves basically creating an understanding of each country and splitting what's happening in that country into a series of trends. For example, in the US she talks about cocooning, and by that she means that the world's getting to be a dangerous place and everyone's going back into their homes and so anything which is a delivery service to your home will become popular.

There's also of course down-aging, where everyone when they are 50 wants to look like Jane Fonda, and so on. And so, you can then use all of these trends and you would work all of these strands together in order to try and develop an understanding of what would happen in the future. Is there anything that you can think of that...oh and... the fourth aspect was just pure brainstorming.

Are there any ideas that you could come up with, do you think, which would help you anticipate what would be happening in the future in order to launch new products?

Audio Two (8.11)

Speaker 1   I think one of the ideas that's coming out of Japan at the moment in manufacturing technology is the idea of mass customization. Up until now, we've always talked about mass standardization, millions of units of identical product, whereas now it's very much the emphasis on designing something for each individual customer and being able to produce it using the same mass production techniques that they've used in the past. We've had an example of mass customized bicycles in Japan, where there are over a million different options that you can choose by specifying your choice of bicycle frame, of handlebar grip, of saddle size, colour of the bicycle, and that bicycle will be made for you in the same amount of time that they would have taken to make a mass produced bicycle, say, ten years ago.

Speaker 2   Do you think, there is actually an interesting antithesis to that though, which is that in the car industry, one could argue that there has been mass customization for some time. You can specify colour, seat trims, all sorts of aspects, and again I've heard a statistic which seems hard to believe, that Rover Group produce a quarter million different models given all the paint colours and so on, but when Toyota produced the Lexus, they gave you no option. They really reduced the number of options down to almost nothing, down to basically the paint colour, and they've just said, that we are giving you all the options, so you have no option. In a sense it seems like the car manufacturers in order to slimline production are trying to go the other way. And do you think there are some industries where, although I accept what you are saying about bicycles and certain other products, do you think there are some industries where, in fact mass customization is going to reduce in a sense, and all they are going to do is to give you everything they possible could give you, because it's simpler to manufacture that way?

Chapter Nine: Environmental awareness

Audio One (9.2)

Speaker 1   Now James, certainly technology has had a big impact on the defence industry, and in particular it has a lot of problems to do with pollution.

Speaker 2   Yes, my background was in the Royal Air Force and in particular, in military aviation, there are two principal pollution problems. One of them is noise, and one of them is fuel. To take noise first, obviously people practise flying lower and lower and faster and faster as the technology in aircraft has improved, for example, flying low level now in Tornado bombers is usually done at 250 feet and 420 knots and they do have the capability of going as low as 50 feet. However, the noise that one of these aircraft puts out is quite phenomenal. You don't notice it coming until it's past you and this can impact really quite severely, particularly on farmers' livelihoods – and in those terms it would be, for example, chicken farmers with chickens in closed coops, they can kill themselves by dashing themselves against the sides of the buildings when an aircraft passes and also when cows and sheep and other animals are in lambing or giving birth, and quite sensitive times in their natural cycle through the year.

Similarly, there can be quite severe problems in wildlife sanctuaries, with birds in particular, when they are nesting and feeding, and when there are large swarms of them. Not only can the aircraft obviously destroy these birds if it hits them, but a single bird will bring down an aircraft too at a cost of around £25 million per time and that doesn't take account of the lives of the pilots as well. So noise pollution has been a real problem and there's now increasing agitation amongst a lot of rural people and quite a lot of political effort to actually stop flying happening at low-level and, in fact, this has been banned completely in Germany for example; and, there is talk of it happening here. What we are doing now, is the Air Force is flying more and more in remote regions of the world like Canada and Alaska, although, of course this is just exporting the problem.

Audio Two (9.10)

Speaker 1   Has there been much advance in the technology of aeronautics to lower noise pollution?

Speaker 2   Yes, there is actually, and that is in use in civil aircraft particularly, and you'll notice now when you are flying in civil aircraft that your takeoff and descents are much, much steeper than they used to be. I don't know if you have noticed that, but that is one of the reasons, because of course, the steeper you can climb away from the ground, the less noise there'll be for a large radius surrounding the area.

The other thing they do is they put a baffle over the rear of the engine. The reason engines make noise, is because air molecules are rushing out of the back of the jet and they're scraping against the still air molecules which are just existing in the surrounding air, and it's that friction between the moving air molecules and the still air that creates noise. So, what they do is they create a baffle which is essentially a circle around the rear of the jet, but in a very wiggly shape and what that does is it increases the whole surface area, and so therefore, the more surface area you can have between the surrounding molecules, the less overall speed and friction you actually end up having.

So, that's a way of reducing it and when you hear about civil aircraft being fitted with noise reduction, that's what they're doing. They are putting a baffle on the back of the jet which essentially tries to reduce the friction between molecules coming out of the back of the jet and the surrounding air.

Speaker 1   I know within office technology, there's been a lot of advances lately using white noise generation, where you will have a microphone that will pick up the noise that is being generated and it will do the absolute opposite in terms of the waves. Has there been anything like that in aeronautics?

Speaker 2   Yes, there has in helicopters. Westland have created new helicopters now. Helicopters, I don't know if you have ever flown in one, but it is like sitting in a badly balanced washing machine. They are very, very noisy, there is lots of vibration. They can be really very uncomfortable over long periods, and that's because the rotors are setting up such intense vibrations around the air frame that each of these bits of metal are vibrating and creating noise. And what Westland have done, is they have created a whole bunch of these points, as you said, with little microphones and little reverse motors and they create opposite vibrations.

              However, the downside to that is that there's no testing yet on just how much this fatigues the air frame, because this could increase the fatigue life enormously. Aircraft last in terms of fatigue hours, it's called, and every time you go flying, there's fatigue meters all over the aircraft and they read off the readings when you land and that goes off against the aircraft's maintenance chart and it ticks off fatigue life. So if you have a very nice gentle smooth flight, it will use hardly any fatigue life, if you go through lots of turbulence, lots of bad weather, it uses up lots of fatigue life for the same flight time.

              And so, sometimes aircraft will be retired out of service after only five years, because they've been bashed about, whereas others will up there after 30/40 years, and it's simply that they have been flown more gently or have been lucky and have been flying in smooth air.

Chapter Ten: Getting about and keeping in touch

Audio One (10.9)

Speaker 1   There has been a lot of talk lately, about the move towards working at home, that the whole technological revolution is allowing people through having home computers, through improved communication networks on the telephone, through such things as fax machines, to be able to take the whole office environment, do it at home and thus not have to move or transport themselves to the downtown core anymore. Rather interestingly, there's been some recent research showing that people don't actually like it working at home, because they are all alone. So I think what you are going to see in the future is sort of a combination of trends. Certainly the technology is allowing you to break up the central office and move things out, but I think you're still going to see people working in offices. It just might be slightly closer to home.

Speaker 2   Yes, in a sense, don't you think one of the problems of society, and in terms of consumption of fuels and in terms of unpleasantness of commuting, is really that we've built up cities where there are work sections and then there are suburbs with homes and ideally, if you were starting from scratch again, you'd have a city which mixed everything, so that private homes were right next to offices which were right next to shops. So in a sense one of the reasons, it seemed to me, that people wanted to start working at home, is because they couldn't stand commuting and they didn't have to spend two or three hours a day on the train and buses or whatever. But you could also avoid that just by better town planning, and so people could enjoy the social interaction that they have at work, but they wouldn't have to face the commute.

Speaker 1   I think that that's it entirely, movement back towards the village.

Speaker 2   But, do you think that is ever achievable in, for example, North America, which is just such a car-obsessed culture and in which long drives are really quite standard?

Speaker 1   I think that if it's possible anywhere in the world, it's likely going to be North America, simply because there has been the movement away from the cities. Right now, the only reason people do go into the cities is to go to work, if the work moves out of the downtown core, they still get their car and maybe they only drive for five minutes instead of fifty now.

Chapter Eleven: Communications and work

Audio One (11.2)

Speaker 1   A lot has been written and said about how PCs have enhanced personal productivity. And no one can argue with the fact that PCs have forever changed how we, as individuals, work. But has the PC really changed the way our businesses work? Do we really run our businesses any differently because of them? I don't think so. The PC has only changed the way individuals work, and I believe that the real pay-off will come when the PC helps to run our businesses better, which in this age of look-alike products means, faster. To conduct business faster, we must get information from one place to another faster. Just look at the explosion in the growth of services that are based on doing this. Fax, cellular phone, overnight delivery, 24-hour cable news – why did these things grow so rapidly? Because the success of a business depends on being able to ship information around faster than the competition.

As the pace of business picks up we come to the threshhold of "just in time" business. Where getting the right information where it's needed quickly will become a competitive advantage, perhaps the only significant competitive advantage in the years ahead. So we need to examine what it will take to enable the PC to help us reach this goal of "just in time" business. But before we can address that question, there's an even more basic question ahead of us: Is the PC the right tool for the job, or has it finally reached its limits? A lot of people are saying that the PC of today is falling behind in some key capabilities. What are they? First they say: it's not powerful enough for graphics. Second: networking PCs requires an act of God! And third: the machines become obsolete too quickly. I have to concede that these have been weak areas in the past for the PC architecture, but this rugged industry of ours is once again rising to the challenge.

Let's look at each of these areas in more detail. It is useful to recall how graphics evolved on the PC. The first PC was designed to work with text only. Over time, colour and improved resolution became available, coupled with faster processors which led to the development of richer applications. However, while microprocessor performance has increased rapidly from generation to generation, graphics performance has evolved much more slowly.

Audio Two (11.16)

Speaker 1 To network our universe we must overcome three problems. Networks are hard to build, networks are hard to maintain, and networks, once they are installed, are unmanageable. Today networks everywhere are functioning only because we have thrown people at them – network administrators. I walked around the building where I work and counted, we have just about one network administrator for every network in operation. Now estimates say there will be some 11 million networks in use by 1995, if we have to have one network administrator for each of these 11 million networks, let's say at $50,000, per network administrator, it would cost more than $550 billion – twice next year's defence budget. Even with the peace dividend, this is not likely to happen.

Let me compare this with a different situation. Today the network industry is where the telephone industry was some 50 years ago. If the telephone industry had not changed the way it worked, every man, woman and child would have had to end up as a telephone operator to cope with today's traffic. But as you can see in this chart, things did change. During the 1970s, when computerized switching started, the number of operators began to drop. Another way to look at this is that every man, woman and child, every phone user, did, in fact, become a phone operator. Taking the telephone analogy a step further, imagine what our desks would look like today if the telephone industry had developed the same way as PC networking. There would be a different phone for different types of phone calls. Our challenge is, then, to make PC networks as simple to use as a telephone network, and the best way to do this is to throw, not people, but technology at the problem.

Chapter Twelve: Inner and outer space

Audio One (12.7)

Speaker 1   Another example of this is actually in the software business. I didn't mention that there's a whole industry already out there which is almost as big as any other industry in the world – which is computer games, where Sega and Nintendo obviously dominate – but that's another model if you like, of how the future can evolve in terms of a device that interacts, and actually some of the most advanced software in the world is right now written for games consoles and you can imagine, for example, extending that into all walks of life, public and private – and just one example of that recently I heard about a software piece that using very advanced hardware as described in the media discussion about hardware will – they want to offer you a virtual nightclub, for example, which sounds crazy, but actually if you think about this you can do virtually anything – virtually virtual anything – which is an interesting concept.

I mean in a nightclub, for example, you can obviously in a virtual space enter the nightclub, find dancing partners, go to the bar and get a drink, discuss the latest fashion with fashion designers, talk to rockstars and pop musicians – all in virtual space, of course – and many other things which I don't want to mention that we do at nightclubs, but the idea here is what you're building is a world inside the computer that becomes a way of you interacting within the environment which normally in a computer sense you think you're only a passive part of this, because traditional computers have been passive.

But when the computer can simulate using its hardware and software technology for virtual space, then you can create almost anything – that way, as long as you have the imagination and the money. And so then you can transmit that anywhere in the world and, as Yolanta said, you can share this with anybody in the world as well so, it's not just you going to this nightclub, it's you and your friends maybe 10,000 miles away, in principle, in the same nightclub. And that's just an example, that's the sort of model, and you can extend that to anything in the home and in the office and out in the streets.

Answer Key

1.3

The **overexploitation** of natural resources and the environmental changes that the earth seems to be **undergoing** present serious dangers to mankind. Although many feel that the threat of global warming has been **overstated**, there is no doubt that the **underlying** processes cause widespread concern. These issues are particularly significant for the world's **underdeveloped** regions. For example, the **overuse** of land for farming and the destruction of tropical forests may set off climatic changes which could ultimately **overwhelm** the environment. Fortunately, the publicity given to these matters has increased our **understanding** of the threat and our awareness of the human **undertaking** involved. Our responsibility for natural resources cannot be **overlooked**.

1.13

1   The introduction of advanced technologies is no guarantee either of their success or (of) their stability.
2   However, people frequently do not have that opportunity.
3   Users are denied the opportunity to become choosers because nobody seeks their opinions.

1.14

1   The company was fined heavily for dumping hazardous waste.
2   Environmental issues have become a major concern among the developed countries.
3   The World Bank's report called for increased agricultural research.
4   Most technological development makes some kind of demand on its users.
5   One of the World Bank's objectives is to promote economic stability.

1.18

The arguments **put forward** by Bruce Rich start from his view that the World Bank's policies have **set back** economic progress in developing societies and may even have **brought about** their cultural decline. Western-style planning has **opened up** much land for commercial exploitation but has in the process **driven out** the communities that lived there. Rich argues that centralised development cannot **take on** the problems of the developing world in any effective way; he believes that a network of agencies should be **set up** to **deal with** the task of funding suitable technologies for these societies.

1.19

para 1	delegate
para 2	accomplice
para 3	technocratic
	top-down planning
	devastated
para 4	low-impact technologies
	accessible

2.8

1 Not only grapes but also mangoes and melons... (para 3)
2 The São Francisco is pure gold... (para 4)
3 High temperatures and low humidity levels make fruits sweeter and richer. (para 4)
4 ...the vineyards irrigated by the São Francisco river. (para 1)
5 The workers...resume pruning. (para 2)

2.9

1 He has a Canadian-born wife.
2 Many cars are now assembled by remote-controlled robots.
3 He heard a blood-curdling scream.
4 He has a French-speaking girlfriend.
5 Only fully-guaranteed cars are sold here.
6 This is a two-man job.

2.10

1 pitch
2 wide
3 crystal
4 rock
5 solid

2.15

1 The delta of the river Guadalquivir, where more than half of Europe's bird species can be found, has been damaged by irrigation projects.
2 Environmentalists, who are shocked by the sheer scale of the plan, claim it is 'ecologically nonsensical'.
3 The plan, which would cost hundreds of billions of pesetas to implement, involves building dams, roads, flood defence works and oil pipelines.
4 The European Commission, which is based in Brussels, is considering funding a vast dam scheme in Spain.
5 EU money would be used to prepare the Sierra Nevada ski area, where the 1995 World Championships are being held.

2.16

1 A paleozoologist examines fossilized animals.
2 An entomologist studies insects.
3 A seismologist is an expert on earthquakes.
4 An astrophysicist is interested in stars and related phenomena.
5 A pathologist performs post-mortems on dead bodies.
6 A meteorologist studies the weather.
7 A parapsychologist is concerned with telepathy and clairvoyance.
8 An ornithologist is interested in and studies birds.

3.12

1 The turbine floats on a hollow concrete hull and would be moored to anchors by polyester ropes.
2 A vision of rows of turbines, standing on high ground and visible for miles, has split environmentalist opinion.
3 Stage 2 of the programme, building a prototype offshore turbine, will cost up to £3 million.
4 Although expensive, offshore wind farms have advantages over land-based farms.
5 A gun that will only fire when held by a designated user is now being developed.

3.15

1 What you see when you switch on the machine... (para 4)
2 ...gauges the usability of its devices by inviting people into the laboratory to try them out. (para 5)
3 ...founded in 1990 by Mark Porat, Bill Atkinson and Andy Herzfeld... (para 2)
4 ...so beloved of 1950s science fiction – a communicator. (para 1)
5 ...pick the building offering the service you want. (para 4)

3.16

1 The shoes he was wearing were worn out.
2 He's overweight and unfit.
3 The Cabinet Minister lied.
4 I'd like to buy the Ferrari, but I can't afford it/I haven't got enough money.
5 Three men were expelled from the country yesterday for spying.
6 'This will hurt,' said the dentist.
7 The estate agent's details said that the house was in a poor condition/falling down.
8 If you don't pay me what you owe me, I'll sue you.

4.6

1 Microcontrollers emerged in the mid-seventies.
2 The use of ASICs rose in 1982.
3 Chip design tools that were capable of customizing high-end microprocessors emerged in 1993.
4 It is predicted that by 1999 better design tools and chips of between 50 and 100 million transistors will allow product designers to crank out systems-on-a-chip.

4.11

1(a) The computer was very easy to use, but he couldn't use it.
1(b) He was an expert in computers, but he couldn't use this one.

2(a) She learned lots of things on holiday, including how to swim.
2(b) It is a surprise that she learned to swim, because she is frightened of water.

3(a) He remembered everything about her, including her name.
3(b) It is a surprise that he remembered her name, because he has a terrible memory for names.

4.12

1 It is difficult, even for the highly computer-literate, to estimate the needs of network users.
2 It is not easy, even for the most determined, to give up smoking.
3 It is possible, even for people with poor memories, to learn a foreign language.
4 It is easy, even for the most uncoordinated, to drive an automatic car.
5 It is impossible, even for the very athletic, to run as fast as a cheetah.
6 It is a challenge, even for specialists in electronics, to forecast the growth of one-chip systems.

5.8

1 technological
2 hierarchical
3 theoretical
4 practical
5 critical
6 pedagogical

5.10

1, 2, and 3 should be selected

5.11

1 Digital information gives users the opportunity to control and change the information they consume.
2 According to Negroponte, today's TV set is the least intelligent appliance in the home.
3 Up to now most convergent developments have been influenced more by business priorities than by domestic needs.
4 Negroponte's convergent technologies concept is intended to give consumers the greatest freedom.
5 Open television will enable viewers to watch news bulletins when they require such a service.

5.12

1 Forgetting to record the TV programme meant that Julia missed her favourite soap opera.
2 Choosing when they watch TV programmes will enable consumers to control their own viewing patterns.
3 Interacting with their televisions means, for example, that viewers can change the ending of films.
4 Asking his boss for a pay rise got Harry the sack.

5.13

1 run out of
2 caught up with
3 get on with
4 look forward to
5 get rid of
6 take care of

5.15

Traditionally, computer programmers have used **procedural** methods in program design, defining elements in high-level computer-based languages which are not **related** to human languages or **real-world** entities. In object-based applications, the emphasis is on the desired end result rather than on the processes **required** to reach such a result; in other words, the approach is practical and intuitive, focusing on real-world **priorities** in systems designed (say) to meet business needs. Software components can therefore be reused and **recombined** like pieces of Lego to create programs customised to the needs of the users.

6.6

Influenza, or flu, is an acute **viral** infection. Its main **symptoms** are fever, fatigue, headache, pains in the joints and loss of **appetite**. Many cases of flu are quite mild, although often **severe (serious)** enough to necessitate absence from work. Some attacks are much more **serious (severe)**, particularly if a **secondary** viral infection occurs. Influenza tends to come in waves because new **strains** prove resistant to the body's **immune** system and to **vaccines** used against **previous** forms of the disease.

6.13

2, 3, 4, 5, 6, and 7 should be selected

6.16

1 The government responded with drastic measures, ordering emission inspections for all vehicles.
2 There is a 23 percent loss of oxygen at this altitude, making combustion processes less efficient.
3 The authorities introduced lead-free petrol, reducing lead levels by four-fifths.
4 Mexico could enjoy the prospect of greater prosperity, making the creation of cleaner environments all the more necessary.
5 The city's population increased to nineteen million, making it one of the world's largest conurbations.

6.17

1 overwork
2 anti-smoking
3 dissatisfied
4 unbelievable
5 disinclined

7.8

1 What is far less certain, though, is the effect that such a temperature rise will have on society. (para 1)
2 The melting of polar ice would swell the oceans, invading low-lying farmland... (para 4)
3 As warmer air holds more water vapour... (para 3)
4 ...the reduction will be more serious in the developing economies... (para 5)
5 Temperature rises in tropical and subtropical areas, where some crops already approach their limit of heat tolerance,... (para 4)

7.11

1 In increasing the size of their fishing fleets, many developing countries are repeating the rich countries' mistakes.
2 Without delivering the plenty they promised, managers have curbed the fishermen's independence.
3 Having peaked in the 1960s, cod catches off the northwest coast of the US collapsed in the 1970s.
4 After turning back because of the weather, the aircraft dumped its fuel.
5 After closing the valves to the gas pipeline, all the engineers could do was to burn the gas off.

7.12

1	cause	6	effect
2	blame	7	result
3	blame	8	limit
4	caused	9	extent
5	result	10	extent

8.3

1 para 1 fixed
2 para 1 conventional wisdom
3 para 3 read-out
4 para 4 throw a spanner in the works
5 para 3 coefficient
6 para 1 intuition
7 para 4 instantaneously

8.4

2, 4 and 6 should be selected

8.5

1 never
2 already
3 ever
4 for
5 yet
6 since

8.9

1 consumer research – asking people in the street
2 survey of experts – asking specialists
3 looking at regional trends – geographical analysis
4 brainstorming – discussing random ideas

8.13

A
1 What I think he is doing is working too hard.
2 What new approaches to manufacturing are doing is increasing customer choice.
3 What Rover are doing is offering a quarter million different models.
4 What a small calculator does is produce a read-out.
5 What brainstorming does is help business planners to formulate ideas.

B Possible answers:
1 What professional gamblers are doing is finding new ways to beat the odds.
2 What customization does is provide greater choice for the customer.
3 What standardization does is limit the options available to customers.

8.16

1 Is it possible to predict the behaviour of financial markets?
2 It has been known for a long time that fluctuations in the financial markets are not unpredictable.
3 Three developments have resulted from the explosion in automated trading.
4 The computer program will need to be updated on a regular basis.

8.17

to pick

1 picked two sides
2 pick his pocket
3 pick her brains
4 picked a fight
5 pick holes in his argument
6 pick a winner

8.18

1 economist
2 scientist
3 chemist
4 meteorologist
5 astronomer
6 linguist

9.6

1 ...dysentery and diarrhea... (para 3)
2 Ethiopia and elsewhere in the Third World... (para 5)
3 The British-based charity WaterAid... (para 2)
4 ...the work at Hitosa isn't just about saving the villagers the long walk. It includes health education and training... (para 4)

9.7

1 How was the money for the project obtained?
2 In all, it was a four-hour trip each way.
3 The result will be a permanent water supply, better health for the community and lower child mortality.
4 £200 is required to hire a skilled mason, half coming from donations and half from local contributions.
5 Never before has the charity supported so large and ambitious a project.

9.12

1, 4 and 6 should be selected

9.14

1, 2, 3, 5 and 6 should be selected

9.17

Possible answers:

1 Many feel that by sponsoring development projects the West is trying to make its peace with the Third World.
2 It was thought to be one of the most enterprising charities in the country, but overspending proved to be its downfall.
3 Zimbabwe is often considered to be a country which can supply the rest of southern Africa with food staples.
4 Rich Western companies that refuse to donate to developing-world charities could be said to be greedily guarding resources which they are not using.
5 If you're running a charity, you must ensure that as much money as possible reaches the people you want to help, so you must cut down on your expenditures.
6 Populations accustomed to going short of food may be resentful of societies that enjoy a luxurious and carefree way of life.

10.3

1 City management is becoming more and more ineffective as the poor are trapped in isolated ghettos from which they cannot easily escape.
2 The economic advantages of the city are increasingly questioned as city workers are becoming less productive and are not offered cheaper and swifter transport.
3 Urban management is becoming a paradox as it enables a minority of people to enjoy swift travel while not making similar advantages available to most city dwellers.

10.7

1 ...traffic volume on the main roads has been growing at between 15 and 20 percent per year. (para 4)
2 Traffic conditions in Bangkok are generally recognized as being among the worst in the world. (para 1)
3 ...and many small local access roads or *soi*. (para 5)
4 ...have 'frozen' substantial areas of land from development since access to the surrounding road networks is lacking. (para 3)
5 ...in this metropolis of nine million (fourteen percent of the country's population)... (para 2)

10.12

1, 2, 3, 5 and 6 should be selected

10.13

1 Underground railway systems have been under construction for some years in many cities but are still a long way from being operational.
2 The transport challenge is one of the most serious problems cities in the developing world have to contend with.
3 The number of privately-owned cars has shown a sharp rise.
4 Digital communications offer the possibility of a world in which you need never lose touch.

10.15

1 well-founded
2 cost-conscious
3 well-kept
4 half-hearted
5 ill-advised
6 easy-going
7 high-speed

11.4

2, 3 and 5 should be selected

11.5

fax
cellular telephones
overnight delivery
24-hour cable news

11.8

Possible answers:

1 gadgets
2 imagine
3 worldwide
4 plan
5 re-design their trademark
6 proliferation

11.10

1 done away with
2 making do with
3 make sure
4 do without
5 made up
6 do damage
7 make way for

11.13

2, 3, 5 and 6 should be selected

11.14

1 setting up
2 wiped out
3 laying off
4 pointed out
5 falling behind

12.3

epiphenomenon – a side effect
emergent property – an ongoing process that feeds itself
dementia – a mental illness
cerebral cortex – the outer layer of the brain
introspection – thinking about oneself

12.5

Possible answers:
1 hypothetical situation
2 theoretical knowledge
3 experimental one-way system
4 conscious effort
5 original manuscripts

12.11

1 para 1 and 3
2 para 3
3 para 4   …a grim entropic chill…
4 para 5   …data…
5 para 2   …our universe erupted in a Big Bang 15 billion years ago…

12.12

1 Stars and galaxies might collapse, creating a huge fireball that will consume everything.
2 There was a Big Bang 15 billion years ago, exploding all the matter and energy in the universe.
3 Evidence suggests that there is more matter than is actually visible to astronomers, raising the issue of the ultimate fate of the universe.
4 If the universe contains a lot of matter, gravitational forces will pull back the stars and galaxies, eventually destroying them.

12.15

to keep
1 kept under lock and key
2 keep the peace
3 keep their distance
4 keeping…under control
5 keep an eye on
6 keep their heads above water

12.17

1, 2 and 5 should be selected

Acknowledgements

We are grateful for permission to use copyright material as follows:

The European newspaper © 1994, all rights reserved.
Ícaro, the magazine of Varig Brazilian Airways © 1994, all rights reserved.
New Scientist magazine © 1994, all rights reserved.
The Observer newspaper © 1994, all rights reserved.
Small World, the magazine of Intermediate Technology Development Group
The Urban Age, published by the World Bank 1994.
Robbie the Robot © 1956 Turner Entertainment Co., all rights reserved.

We wish to thank the following individuals and organizations:

Geoffrey Matthews (series editor)
Simon and Sue Bright (subject consultants)
Frank Devlin (illustrations)
James Martin, David Bulman, Annabel Tribe, Adam Lacy-Hulbert, Andy Grove,
Sir Anthony Cleaver, Jolante Pilecka, David Lyon, Sven Oernfeldt (audio contributors)
Ken Singleton (language exercises)
Business Sound
Octagon Communications Group
Studio AVP

Bayer AG
Cambridge University Biochemistry Department
Hewlett-Packard
IBM UK
Intel Corporation
Symbol Technologies
WaterAid
The World Bank

This course has been developed in association with:

**The Training Store Limited,
1 High Street,
Maidenhead,
Berks SL6 1JN,
England**